THE INTERNATIONAL ENCYCLOPEDIA OF PHYSICAL CHEMISTRY AND CHEMICAL PHYSICS

Topic 11. THE IDEAL CRYSTALLINE STATE

EDITOR: M. BLACKMAN

Volume 1

APPLICATIONS OF NEUTRON DIFFRACTION IN CHEMISTRY

THE INTERNATIONAL ENCYCLOPEDIA
OF PHYSICAL CHEMISTRY AND CHEMICAL PHYSICS

THE INTERNATIONAL ENCYCLOPEDIA
OF PHYSICAL CHEMISTRY AND CHEMICAL PHYSICS

Editors-in-Chief

E. A. GUGGENHEIM   J. E. MAYER
READING   LA JOLLA

F. C. TOMPKINS
LONDON

Chairman of the Editorial Advisory Group

ROBERT MAXWELL
PUBLISHER AT PERGAMON PRESS

List of Topics and Editors

1. Mathematical Techniques — H. JONES, *London*
2. Classical and Quantum Mechanics — R. McWEENY, *Keele*
3. Electronic Structure of Atoms — C. A. HUTCHINSON, JR., *Chicago*
4. Molecular Binding — J. W. LINNETT, *Oxford*
5. Molecular Properties
   (a) Electronic — J. W. LINNETT, *Oxford*
   (b) Non-Electronic — N. SHEPPARD, *Cambridge*
6. Kinetic Theory of Gases — E. A. GUGGENHEIM, *Reading*
7. Classical Thermodynamics — D. H. EVERETT, *Bristol*
8. Statistical Mechanics — J. E. MAYER, *La Jolla*
9. Transport Phenomena — J. C. McCOUBREY, *Birmingham*
10. The Fluid State — J. S. ROWLINSON, *London*
11. The Ideal Crystalline State — M. BLACKMAN, *London*
12. Imperfections in Solids — Editor to be appointed
13. Mixtures, Solutions, Chemical and phase Equilibria — M. L. McGLASHAN, *Reading*
14. Properties of Interfaces — D. H. EVERETT, *Bristol*
15. Equilibrium Properties of Electrolyte Solutions — R. A. ROBINSON, *Washington, D.C.*
16. Transport Properties of Electrolytes — R. H. STOKES, *Armidale*
17. Macromolecules — C. E. H. BAWN, *Liverpool*
18. Dielectric and Magnetic Properties — J. W. STOUT, *Chicago*
19. Gas Kinetics — A. TROTMAN-DICKENSON, *Aberystwyth*
20. Solution Kinetics — R. M. NOYES, *Eugene*
21. Solid and Surface Kinetics — F. C. TOMPKINS, *London*
22. Radiation Chemistry — R. S. LIVINGSTON, *Minneapolis*

APPLICATIONS OF NEUTRON DIFFRACTION IN CHEMISTRY

BY

G. E. BACON

ATOMIC ENERGY RESEARCH ESTABLISHMENT

HARWELL

PROFESSOR OF PHYSICS (ELECT)

UNIVERSITY OF SHEFFIELD

A Pergamon Press Book

THE MACMILLAN COMPANY
NEW YORK

1963

THE MACMILLAN COMPANY
60 Fifth Avenue
New York 11, N.Y.

This book is distributed by
THE MACMILLAN COMPANY
pursuant to a special arrangement with
PERGAMON PRESS LIMITED
Oxford, England.

Library of Congress Card Number 63–10102

SET IN MODERN SERIES 7 BY SANTYPE LTD., SALISBURY, WILTS.,
AND PRINTED IN GREAT BRITAIN BY BARNICOTTS, TAUNTON, SOMERSET

INTRODUCTION

THE International Encyclopedia of Physical Chemistry and Chemical Physics is a comprehensive and modern account of all aspects of the domain of science between chemistry and physics, and is written primarily for the graduate and research worker. The Editors-in-Chief, Professor E. A. GUGGENHEIM, Professor J. E. MAYER and Professor F. C. TOMPKINS, have grouped the subject matter in some twenty groups (General Topics), each having its own editor. The complete work consists of about one hundred volumes, each volume being restricted to around two hundred pages and having a large measure of independence. Particular importance has been given to the exposition of the fundamental bases of each topic and to the development of the theoretical aspects; experimental details of an essentially practical nature are not emphasized although the theoretical background of techniques and procedures is fully developed.

The Encyclopedia is written throughout in English and the recommendations of the International Union of Pure and Applied Chemistry on notation and cognate matters in physical chemistry are adopted. Abbreviations for names of journals are in accordance with *The World List of Scientific Periodicals*.

CONTENTS

PREFACE

THE purpose of this book is to give an account of the contribution which neutron-diffraction methods have made to the solution of problems in chemistry and the main aim is to describe the new knowledge which has been obtained. Descriptions of the nature of neutron scattering and the details of experimental techniques are therefore restricted to what is necessary to indicate the type of problem which can be solved and the nature of the sample material which is required for study. An attempt is made to show that although opportunities for participating in this kind of work are narrowly restricted by the need for a high-flux nuclear-reactor, nevertheless the results obtained so far have given interesting and important information in many different branches of chemistry. The author's justification, as a physicist, for writing this account is to say that he is describing a physical technique which is especially suited to solving chemical problems and that there is no boundary line between the two disciplines in the study of solids and liquids.

Thanks are due to the many authors and authorities who have permitted the use of diagrams from their papers and publications, especially to the American Institute of Physics and the Editors of *Acta Crystallographica* and *Physical Review*, who together have published such a large proportion of the papers on this subject, and to Dr. B. O. Loopstra for two figures from his Ph.D. thesis at the University of Amsterdam. The sources, and authors, of these illustrations are indicated in their individual legends. Figure 8.6 comes from the paper "X-ray and neutron diffraction studies of molten alkali halides" in Vol. 79 of the *Annals of the New York Academy of Sciences*.

Goring.   G. E. BACON.

CHAPTER 1

PRINCIPLES AND METHODS

1.1. X-ray Crystallography

In 1912 Von Laue demonstrated that a crystal would act as a diffraction grating for X-rays, thus showing that X-rays had the properties of a wave-motion. Immediately afterwards this discovery was used, particularly by W. L. Bragg, for the complementary purpose of investigating the three-dimensional structure of crystals by examining the way in which they diffracted beams of X-rays. In the simplest type of experimental measurement, a polycrystalline or powdered sample is examined in a beam of monochromatic X-rays. From the angular positions of the diffraction halos, which are produced, the size and shape of the unit of pattern or fundamental building block of the crystal can be deduced. A more elaborate, but much more informative procedure, is to study the diffraction from a single crystal and obtain a pattern of spectra in three dimensions. From measurements of the intensities of the spectra in patterns of this sort the electron density at any point in the "unit cell" can be expressed as a three-dimensional Fourier series. The detailed way in which this can be done is described in standard books on X-ray crystallography,[1] and the reader who is unfamiliar with these methods and wishes to understand the procedure in detail should consult one of these. For our present purpose we will simply indicate the relation between the intensity of the spectra and the spatial content of the unit-cell by a one-dimensional analogy. In Fig. 1.1 we show the diffraction of monochromatic light by an ordinary line diffraction grating. If the transmission factor for the grating has a simple harmonic distribution, as in 1.1 (i), then there will only be two diffracted beams, one on each side of the incident beam at inclinations which depend on the linear period of the grating. If the transmission factor is a regularly repeating square wave, as is usually the case, then there will be a number of spectra on each side with an intensity distribution as shown at (ii). In fact the spectral pattern is the Fourier transform of the transmission factor of the lines in the grating. Conversely, if we measure

1

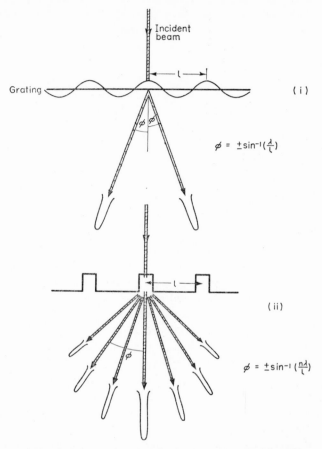

Incident
beam

Grating

$\phi = \pm \sin^{-1}(\frac{\lambda}{l})$

(i)

(ii)

$\phi = \pm \sin^{-1}(\frac{n\lambda}{l})$

FIG. 1.1. The production of spectra by a diffraction grating, illustrating the relation between the distribution of intensity and the transmission factor for the grating line. (i) is for a sinusoidal variation and (ii) is for a regularly repeating square wave.

the amplitudes of the successive spectra then we can express the transmission factor of the grating line by a Fourier series. Our crystal case is simply a three-dimensional extension of this, in which we can express the electron density at any point in the crystal unit cell, which is the counterpart of the grating-line, by a triple Fourier series. We must emphasize two points in connection with this interpretation. First, in order to evaluate the electron density it is necessary to know the *amplitudes* of the spectra (including their sign or phase) and not simply the intensities: there is, unfortunately, no direct way of measuring the phases of the diffracted beams. Secondly, the final outcome of our analysis is a knowledge of the electron density in the crystal unit. This may be extremely detailed, as witnessed by the very elegant 2-dimensional projections of such molecules as Vitamin B_{12}, but it has two particular shortcomings. An atom is represented only by its electrons and no account is taken of the nuclei, so that an atom of hydrogen gets very scant notice compared with a heavy many-electron atom such as lead or uranium. As the second limitation we comment that the picture takes no account of electron spin and thus is not able to distinguish those unpaired electrons which result in magnetic moments on paramagnetic atoms and, in turn, lead to co-operative magnetic phenomena in ferro-, ferri-, and antiferro-magnetic materials.

1.2. Neutron Crystallography

A beam of neutrons shows certain wave properties, with a wavelength λ given by

$$\lambda = h/mv \qquad (1.2.1)$$

where h is Planck's constant, m is the neutron mass and v is its velocity. If we calculate the energy of a "thermal" neutron, that is a neutron which has thermal energy appropriate to room temperature, we find that its wavelength will be about $1\frac{1}{2}$ Å. This is about the same as the average distance apart of atoms in solids and hence is a very suitable wavelength for the observation of diffraction effects: in fact $1 \cdot 54$ Å is the wavelength of the copper $K\alpha$ line which is most commonly used in X-ray crystallography. We should thus expect thermal neutrons to show good diffraction effects when they fall on a crystal and this was indeed demonstrated as long ago as 1936 by Halban and Preiswerk,[2] and by Mitchell and Powers.[3] However, the neutron beams available at that time were far too weak for the diffraction technique to give any worthwhile information about solids. Only the arrival of the nuclear reactor has led to the appearance of neutron beams which are sufficiently intense for making useful diffraction measurements. We must emphasize though that even the most intense beams available from reactors are much less intense, as regards the number of quanta passing through unit area per second, than the X-ray beams given by ordinary X-ray diffraction tubes. This fact, coupled with the scarcity and expense of high flux reactors, means that we must consider in detail what kind of especially worthwhile information about solids can be secured by neutron diffraction methods, but not by any other technique. In particular we must consider whether some of the limitations met in X-ray crystallography can be avoided by using neutrons. We shall be able to draw some conclusions after considering the actual processes by which neutrons are scattered by atoms and we shall give a short general account of this in the following few pages. The reader who wishes for a more detailed treatment is referred to the author's book[4] *Neutron Diffraction* and to the textbooks on neutron and nuclear physics which are listed[5, 6, 7] among the references at the end of this chapter.

1.3. Neutron Scattering

When a beam of neutrons falls on an assembly of atoms it is the nuclei of the atoms which are effective in diverting or "scattering" neutrons out of the beam. The extent of this scattering is measured by the area of obstruction, or "cross-section", which the nucleus presents to the beam, and to a first approximation this increases regularly, but only slowly, with the atomic weight of the atom. This cross-section is not dependent on the wavelength of the incident neutrons. Superimposed on the effect due to the mere physical size of the nucleus is a process known as "resonance" scattering.[4, 5] In order to understand this we can consider that the incident neutron and the target nucleus combine to form a "compound nucleus". Depending on the position of the energy levels in this compound nucleus, it may happen that for thermal neutrons resonance scattering takes place and this is then superimposed on the ordinary scattering due to the nuclear size. As a result it is found that the extent to which atoms scatter neutrons varies rather haphazardly as we go through the Periodic Table from hydrogen to uranium and beyond. We shall discuss the cross-sections in more detail later but for the present we merely emphasize, as Fig. 1.2 illustrates, that within a factor of three or four times, the scattering amplitudes of all atoms for neutrons are about the same. This is in marked contrast to the scattering of X-rays by atoms: in this latter case, where we are dealing with an *electro-magnetic radiation*, it is the extranuclear electrons which are the scatterers with the result, for example, that the scattering amplitude for a uranium atom is ninety-two times as large as that for an atom of hydrogen.

It will be noticed that we have now ascribed to our target nucleus a scattering *amplitude*, which will have both magnitude and phase, instead of simply a scattering cross-section which merely describes the *intensity* of scattered neutrons. More precisely we can say that if we have an incident plane neutron-wave described by a wave function

$$\psi = e^{i\kappa z} \tag{1.3.1}$$

then the wave scattered by a nucleus will be spherically symmetrical and of the form

$$\psi = -(b/r)e^{i\kappa r} \tag{1.3.2}$$

where r is the distance from the nucleus to the point at which the scattered wave is measured. In these two expressions κ, which is equivalent to $2\pi/\lambda$, is the wave-number of the neutron for a wavelength λ. It is the quantity b, which has the dimensions of a length,

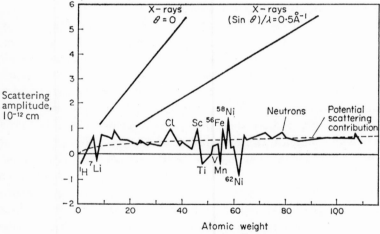

Fig. 1.2. The variation of the scattering amplitude of atoms for neutrons, as a function of their atomic weight. The irregular variation is contrasted with the linear relation for X-rays (from *Research*, 1954, **7**, 297).

which we define as the "scattering length" or "scattering amplitude" of the nucleus (see Refs. 4, 5). Except for the case of a few nuclei which give high *absorption*, as distinct from scattering, b is a real number, although it may have a positive or negative sign, and it is this quantity b which we have plotted in Fig. 1.2. For most nuclei b has a positive sign, which means, from eqn. (1.3.2), that there is a phase-change of 180° between the incident and scattered beams, whereas the much-less-common negative sign means that there is no phase change. In the exceptional cases of high absorption, which we shall not consider further here, b has both real and imaginary components, which expresses the fact that the phase change on scattering is appreciably different from either $0°$ or $180°$.

A more detailed inspection of Fig. 1.2 will show that in certain cases, nickel for example, we have indicated not only the ordinary element but also individual isotopes such as Ni^{58} and Ni^{62} which are indeed credited with widely different values of the scattering length b. These differences arise among the isotopes of certain elements where effects due to resonance scattering are large, because of important differences in the positions of the energy levels for the compound nuclei formed by the various isotopes. Only for a small proportion of elements, particularly the very light ones, the iron-group of transition metals and some of the rare-earth elements, are these large differences among isotopes found to exist. Such differences may be put to useful practical advantages in solving certain crystallograpic problems.

It is of interest to note the absolute values of b as indicated in Fig. 1.2. The order of magnitude is well represented by $0·5 \times 10^{-12}$ cm, and only in very few cases is b less than a half of this value, or greater than twice this. For comparison it may be noted that this same degree of scattering for *X-rays* would be achieved by an atom which contains about two electrons and, since X-ray scattering is proportional to electron content, about ten times this scattering amplitude would be given by calcium which has an atomic number of twenty. Nevertheless, it must be pointed out that whereas the neutron scattering is isotropic, which means that the scattering amplitude is the same at all angles, yet for X-rays it falls away quite quickly as the angle of scattering, between the incident and scattered beams, increases. The different behaviour for neutrons occurs because the nucleus, which is the scattering centre so far as neutrons are concerned, has a diameter of only about 10^{-12} cm and is no more than a point scatterer for a wavelength of 10^{-8} cm. On the other hand the extra-nuclear cloud of electrons, which scatters the X-rays, has dimensions which are about the same as the wavelength of the incident radiation.

1.4. Assemblies of Nuclei

So far we have been considering the scattering of neutrons by single, individual nuclei. In practice, if we are to use neutrons for studying the atomic architecture of solids, we shall have to deal with the scattering by the assembly of nuclei associated with the regular arrangement of atoms in three dimensions which constitute the extended crystal structure. Of primary importance in this consideration is the resultant amplitude of scattering which we get from our unit of pattern, or what we call the "unit cell" of the crystal structure. We can express this resultant, which is called the structure amplitude factor, by making a vector sum of the scattered neutron waves from the various atoms in the unit-cell, in the form

$$- \sum_\rho (b_\rho/r) \, e^{i\kappa r} \, e^{i\rho \cdot \kappa - \kappa'} \qquad (1.4.1)$$

where κ, κ' are the wave-vectors of the neutron before and after scattering. The expression $\exp(i\rho \cdot \kappa - \kappa')$ arises by taking into account the phase differences which arise between the components of radiation scattered by the various different atoms in the unit cell. ρ is the vector drawn from the origin to any particular one of the ρ atoms in the unit cell for which the summation is made. In an extended crystallite, which contains many unit cells, it can readily be shown that there will only be a significant scattered amplitude if the resultant contributions from the individual unit cells support and reinforce each other, as will be the case if the neutron paths for neighbouring unit cells differ from one another by an integral number of wavelengths. This means that diffracted beams will appear only for a specific number of directions $\kappa - \kappa'$, just as the optical spectra from a line diffraction grating only appear at a few discrete angles. An alternative way of regarding this limitation is to say that diffraction takes place only in certain directions for which there is reinforcement between the contributions from successive planes of atoms in the crystal. In this interpretation we write the expression $\exp(i\rho \cdot \kappa - \kappa')$ in the alternative form

$$\exp\{2\pi i(hx/a_0 + ky/b_0 + lz/c_0)\} \qquad (1.4.2)$$

where x, y, z, are the co-ordinates in the unit cell of the particular nucleus ρ; a, b, c are the dimensions of the unit cell and h, k, l are the Miller crystallographic indices appropriate to the particular vector $\kappa - \kappa'$. We then say that we are observing the hkl reflection.

The form of the above expressions (1) and (2) for extended series of atoms would have been exactly the same if we had been considering the diffraction of X-rays. However an important point of difference arises with neutrons when we consider proceeding with the summation in (1) by substituting the appropriate values of b for the various atoms in the unit cell. If we are considering an element which, in the natural state, consists of several isotopes then these individual isotopes will be distributed at random amongst the atomic positions which are assigned to the element. Each isotope will have its own value of b and the effective value of b for substitution in (1) will be the mean value after averaging over the various isotopes, taking into account their relative abundances in the naturally-occurring elements. Thus, as well as a value of scattering length b appropriate to each individual isotope there is a mean value $\bar{b}$ which represents the ordinary element. In addition, it can be shown that there is an isotropic contribution to the background scattering, as distinct from the coherent diffraction peaks. This contribution has an intensity which is proportional to the quantity $\overline{b_r^2} - (\overline{b_r})^2$, where the averaging over b_r^2 and b_r is made over the various isotopes which constitute the element. This background scattering is called "isotopic incoherent scattering" (see Refs. 4, 7) and will be particularly large for elements such as nickel and silver where there are found to be large differences between b values of the abundant isotopes. On the other hand the effect is negligible in the case of elements such as carbon and oxygen which consist almost entirely of a single isotope.

A rather related type of background scattering arises from "spin incoherence".[4] We have already mentioned that the general process of scattering may be considered in terms of a compound nucleus formed by the union of the target nucleus and the incoming neutron. If the nucleus possesses spin I then two alternative compound nuclei can be formed, having spins of $(I + \frac{1}{2})$ and $(I - \frac{1}{2})$ respectively: this happens because the neutron itself has a spin of $\frac{1}{2}$. These two combinations may have different energy levels and, in turn, different scattering lengths b_+, b_- and it can be shown that they have effective abundances equal to $(I + 1)/(2I + 1)$ and $I/(2I + 1)$ respectively. Each atomic site may be regarded as occupied at random by the two species in this proportion and the randomness leads to an incoherent component of scattering in exactly the same way as we noted for a random distribution of isotopes. The most important example of this "spin incoherent scattering" is ordinary hydrogen of unit mass number. Here the values of b_+, b_- are not only quite different in magnitude but they are also opposite in sign, being equal to $+(1 \cdot 04 \times 10^{-12})$ and $-(4 \cdot 7 \times 10^{-12})$ cm respectively. As a result there is a very large amount of incoherent scattering which leads to very substantial background scattering, and which is large enough to be quite troublesome in powder patterns of hydrogen-containing substances. On the other hand the spin incoherent scattering for deuterium is much less important and, whenever possible, it is of advantage to have deuterated samples available if only polycrystalline specimens can be prepared.

We may summarize by saying that the value of b which we must insert in (1) will usually be the mean scattering length for the element, $\bar{b}_r$, where the average is taken over the various isotopes which are present, with allowance being made in each case for the alternative positive and negative spin combinations with respect to the incident neutrons. Collected data for all the elements and isotopes which have been studied so far are given in Table 1.1. The most important quantity which is listed is the scattering length b. Alongside this we show the related quantity $\mathscr{S}$ which is equal to $4\pi b^2$ and represents the total *coherent* scattering cross-section. In the final column we give σ which is the total cross-section for scattering of all kinds, i.e. coherent plus spin-incoherent plus isotope-incoherent. The difference which is usually denoted by s, represents the total incoherent background scattering due to isotope and spin disorder. It can be shown in terms of the previous nomenclature that

$$\sigma = 4\pi\overline{b_r^2}$$
$$\mathscr{S} = 4\pi(\overline{b_r})^2 \quad\quad\quad (1.4.3)$$
$$s = 4\pi\{(\overline{b_r^2}) - (\overline{b_r})^2\}$$

1.5. The Applications of Neutron Diffraction

The particular scope of neutron diffraction which leads to its valuable applications in the solution of chemical problems, especially in crystal chemistry and molecular structure, can now be appreciated.

From either Fig. 1.2 or Table 1.1 it can be seen that the scattering amplitude of hydrogen for neutrons is not much less numerically than the average value for other elements and that it has also the distinguishing feature of being negative in sign. The actual value is $-0\cdot38 \times 10^{-12}$ cm, which can be compared with $0\cdot63 \times 10^{-12}$ cm which is the average numerical value of all the b values listed for elements and isotopes in the table. As a result hydrogen is not much more difficult to locate than any other element, light or heavy. Moreover, if a deuterated compound can be examined then detection and location is made substantially easier and more accurate, for it will be seen that the scattering amplitude of deuterium has the quite substantial value of $0\cdot65 \times 10^{-12}$ cm. Thus, for neutrons, deuterium can be regarded as the average element from the point of view of its scattering amplitude. Other light elements, which offer difficulties with X-rays, when present alongside heavy

TABLE 1.1

Neutron scattering data for elements and isotopes

Element	Atomic number	Atomic weight of natural element	Specific nucleus	Nuclear spin	Neutrons b $(10^{-12}$ cm$)$	$\mathscr{S}$ (barns)	σ (barns)
H	1		^{1}H	$\frac{1}{2}$	$-0\cdot378$	$1\cdot79$	$81\cdot5$
			^{2}H	1	$0\cdot65$	$5\cdot4$	$7\cdot6$
He	2		^{4}He	0	$0\cdot30$	$1\cdot1$	$1\cdot1$
Li	3	$6\cdot94$			$-0\cdot18$	$0\cdot47$	$1\cdot2$
			^{6}Li	1	$0\cdot18$	$0\cdot4$	
			^{7}Li	$\frac{3}{2}$	$-0\cdot21$	$0\cdot6$	$1\cdot4$
Be	4		^{9}Be	$\frac{3}{2}$	$0\cdot774$	$7\cdot53$	$7\cdot54$
B	5						$4\cdot4$
C	6		^{12}C	0	$0\cdot661$	$5\cdot50$	$5\cdot51$
			^{13}C	$\frac{1}{2}$	$0\cdot60$	$4\cdot5$	$5\cdot5$
N	7		^{14}N	1	$0\cdot940$	$11\cdot0$	$11\cdot4$
O	8		^{16}O	0	$0\cdot577$	$4\cdot2$	$4\cdot24$
F	9		^{19}F	$\frac{1}{2}$	$0\cdot55$	$3\cdot8$	$4\cdot0$
Ne	10						$2\cdot9$
Na	11		^{23}Na	$\frac{3}{2}$	$0\cdot351$	$1\cdot55$	$3\cdot4$
Mg	12	$24\cdot3$			$0\cdot52$	$3\cdot60$	$3\cdot70$
Al	13		^{27}Al	$\frac{5}{2}$	$0\cdot35$	$1\cdot5$	$1\cdot5$
Si	14	$28\cdot06$			$0\cdot40$	$2\cdot16$	$2\cdot2$
P	15		^{31}P	$\frac{1}{2}$	$0\cdot53$	$3\cdot5$	$3\cdot6$
S	16		^{32}S	0	$0\cdot31$	$1\cdot2$	$1\cdot2$
Cl	17	$35\cdot5$			$0\cdot99$	$12\cdot2$	$15\cdot0$
Ar	18		^{40}Ar	0	$0\cdot20$	$0\cdot5$	$0\cdot9$
K	19	$39\cdot1$			$0\cdot35$	$1\cdot5$	$2\cdot2$
Ca	20	$40\cdot1$			$0\cdot49$	$3\cdot0$	$3\cdot2$
			^{40}Ca	0	$0\cdot49$	$3\cdot0$	$3\cdot1$
			^{44}Ca	0	$0\cdot18$	$0\cdot4$	
Sc	21		^{45}Sc	$\frac{7}{2}$	$1\cdot18$	$17\cdot5$	$24\cdot0$
Ti	22	$47\cdot9$			$-0\cdot38$	$1\cdot8$	$4\cdot4$
			^{46}Ti	0	$0\cdot48$	$2\cdot90$	
			^{47}Ti	$\frac{5}{2}$	$0\cdot33$	$1\cdot37$	
			^{48}Ti	0	$-0\cdot58$	$4\cdot23$	
			^{49}Ti	$\frac{7}{2}$	$0\cdot08$	$0\cdot08$	
			^{50}Ti	0	$0\cdot55$	$3\cdot80$	
V	23		^{51}V	$\frac{7}{2}$	$-0\cdot05$	$0\cdot032$	$5\cdot1$
Cr	24	$52\cdot0$			$0\cdot352$	$1\cdot56$	$4\cdot1$

b is the scattering amplitude in units of 10^{-12} cm.

$\mathscr{S}$, σ are the coherent and total scattering cross-sections, respectively, in units of 10^{-24} cm^2 (i.e. barns).

Element	Atomic number	Atomic weight of natural element	Specific nucleus	Nuclear spin	b $(10^{-12}$ cm$)$	$\mathscr{S}$ (barns)	σ (barns)
						Neutrons	
Cr			^{52}Cr	0	0·490	3·02	
Mn	25		^{55}Mn	$\frac{5}{2}$	−0·36	1·6	2·0
Fe	26	55·8			0·96	11·4	11·8
			^{54}Fe	0	0·42	2·2	2·5
			^{56}Fe	0	1·01	12·8	12·8
			^{57}Fe		0·23	0·64	2·0
Co	27		^{59}Co	$\frac{7}{2}$	0·25	0·8	6·0
Ni	28	58·7			1·03	13·4	18·0
			^{58}Ni	0	1·44	25·9	
			^{60}Ni	0	0·30	1·1	
			^{62}Ni	0	−0·87	9·5	
Cu	29	63·6			0·79	7·8	8·5
			^{63}Cu	$\frac{3}{2}$	0·67	5·7	
			^{65}Cu	$\frac{3}{2}$	1·11	15·3	
Zn	30	65·4			0·59	4·3	4·2
Ga	31	69·7					7·5
Ge	32	72·6			0·84	8·8	9·0
As	33		^{75}As	$\frac{3}{2}$	0·63	5·0	8·0
Se	34	79·0			0·89	10·0	
Br	35	79·9			0·67	5·7	6·1
Kr	36	82·9					
Rb	37	85·5			0·55	3·8	5·5
Sr	38	87·6			0·57	4·1	10·0
Y	39		^{89}Y	$\frac{1}{2}$	0·80		
Zr	40	91·2			0·62	4·9	6·3
Nb	41		^{93}Nb	$\frac{9}{2}$	0·691	6·0	6·6
Mo	42	95·9			0·661	5·5	6·1
Tc	43						
Ru	44	101·7			0·73	6·68	6·81
Rh	45		^{103}Rh	$\frac{1}{2}$	0·60	4·5	5·6
Pd	46	106·7			0·59	4·4	4·8
Ag	47	107·9			0·61	4·6	6·5
			^{107}Ag	$\frac{1}{2}$	0·83	8·7	10·0
			^{109}Ag	$\frac{1}{2}$	0·43	2·3	6·0
Cd	48	112·4			$0·38 + i0·12$		
In	49	114·8			0·36	1·63	
Sn	50	118·7			0·61	4·6	4·9
Sb	51	121·8			0·54	3·7	4·2
Te	52	127·5			0·56	4·0	4·5
			^{120}Te		0·52	3·4	

Element	Atomic number	Atomic weight of natural element	Specific nucleus	Nuclear spin	Neutrons		
					b (10^{-12} cm)	$\mathscr{S}$ (barns)	σ (barns)
Te			^{123}Te	$\frac{1}{2}$	0·57	4·2	
			^{124}Te		0·55	3·9	
			^{125}Te	$\frac{1}{2}$	0·56	4·0	
I	53		^{127}I	$\frac{5}{2}$	0·52	3·4	3·8
Xe	54	130·2					
Cs	55		^{133}Cs	$\frac{7}{2}$	0·49	3·0	7·0
Ba	56	137·4			0·52	3·4	6·0
La	57		^{139}La	$\frac{7}{2}$	0·83	8·7	9·3
Ce	58	140·25			0·48	2·7	2·7
			^{140}Ce		0·47	2·8	2·6
			^{142}Ce		0·45	2·6	2·6
Pr	59		^{141}Pr	$\frac{5}{2}$	0·44	2·4	4·0
Nd	60	144·3			0·72	6·5	16·0
			^{142}Nd		0·77	7·5	7·5
			^{144}Nd		0·28	1·0	1·0
			^{146}Nd		0·87	9·5	9·5
Pm	61						
Sm	62	150·4					
			^{152}Sm		−0·5	3·0	
			^{154}Sm		0·8	8·0	
Eu	63	152·0					
Gd	64	157·3					
Tb	65		^{159}Tb	$\frac{3}{2}$	0·76		
Dy	66	162·5					
Ho	67		^{165}Ho	$\frac{7}{2}$	0·85	9·1	∼13·0
Er	68	167·6			0·79	7·8	15·0
Tm	69		^{169}Tm	$\frac{1}{2}$			
Yb	70	173·0			1·26		
Lu	71	175·0			0·73		
Hf	72	178·6			0·88	9·7	
Ta	73		^{181}Ta	$\frac{7}{2}$	0·70	6·1	6·0
W	74	183·9			0·466	2·74	5·7
Re	75	186·2			0·92	10·6	
Os	76	190·2			1·12	14·7	14·9
Ir	77	192·2			0·36	1·63	1·66
Pt	78	195·2			0·95	11·2	12·0
Au	79		^{197}Au	$\frac{3}{2}$	0·76	7·3	9·0
Hg	80	200·6			1·3	22·0	26·5
Tl	81	204·4			0·89	10·0	10·1
Pb	82	207·2			0·96	11·5	11·4
Bi	83		^{209}Bi	$\frac{9}{2}$	0·864	9·35	9·37

Element	Atomic number	Atomic weight of natural element	Specific nucleus	Nuclear spin	Neutrons		
					b $(10^{-12}$ cm)	$\mathscr{S}$ (barns)	σ (barns)
Po	84	210·0					
At	85						
Rn	86	222·0					
Fr	87						
Ra	88	226·0					
Ac	89	227·0					
Th	90		^{232}Th	0	0·98	12·3	12·6
Pa	91	231·0					
U	92		^{235}U		0·98		
			^{238}U		0·85	9·0	
Np	93						
Pu	94						

elements, but which can be seen to have favourable scattering amplitudes for neutrons, are carbon, oxygen and nitrogen.

We can also see from Fig. 1.2 that in certain cases, occurring very largely at random, there are large differences between the scattering amplitudes of neighbouring elements, or between certain of their isotopes. This proves to be of great advantage in detecting and measuring chemical ordering in compounds or alloys which contain elements which are near-neighbours, particularly among the iron-group of transition elements, between which it is difficult to distinguish by X-ray methods, without special choice of wavelength for the incident radiation. A further possibility, though one which has not yet been put to use, is the ability to manufacture "invisible" elements, so far as the coherent diffraction of neutrons is concerned, by combining in suitable proportion isotopes which have scattering lengths of opposite sign. Thus, invisible hydrogen, nickel or lithium could be produced and could lead to easier study of the part played by the other components in compounds of these elements.

For completeness we refer at this point to the other main application of neutron diffraction, although this is not primarily of chemical interest and is something which cannot be appreciated from the data in Table 1.1. We have emphasized earlier in this chapter that neutrons are scattered only by the *nuclei* of atoms. This statement is true in most cases but we have to make an exception for atoms which have a resultant magnetic moment. For a fuller account of this subject the reader is referred elsewhere,[4] but we point out here that such "magnetic atoms" cause additional scattering of a neutron beam and this extra scattering is electronic in origin. It is caused by the magnetic electrons, that is those electrons which have unpaired magnetic spins and such as are found, for example, in the ferrous and ferric ions, Fe^{2+} and Fe^{3+}, which possess four and five unpaired electrons respectively. Such atoms or ions have a "magnetic scattering amplitude" p which is directly proportional to their magnetic moment, and can be calculated readily in terms of this moment by the formula

$$p = \left(\frac{e^2\gamma}{mc^2}\right)Sf \qquad (1.5.1)$$

In this expression S is the spin quantum number of the scattering atom, γ is the magnetic moment of the neutron expressed in nuclear magnetons, f is an amplitude form factor, e and m, are the charge and mass of the electron and c is the velocity of light. More correctly we should say that p is the maximum possible value of the magnetic scattering amplitude which is attained for the optimum orientation of the magnetic spin relative to the incident and outgoing neutron beams. The condition which must be satisfied in order to get this maximum scattering is that the atomic magnetic moment should lie in the plane which is perpendicular to the bisector of the tracks of the incident and emergent neutrons: this bisector is usually called the "scattering vector". In the general case the effective scattering amplitude is $p \sin \beta$ where the angle β is indicated in Fig. 1.3. If the magnetic material is in a *para-*

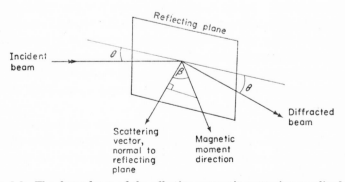

FIG. 1.3. The dependence of the effective magnetic scattering amplitude on the inclination, β, between the scattering vector and the direction of the magnetic moment. Effective amplitude = $p \sin \beta$.

magnetic state then the magnetic scattering will be no more than a further contribution to the background scattering, falling off with increasing angle of scattering according to the magnetic form factor f which takes account of the spatial distribution of the magnetic electrons. On the other hand, when there is an alignment of magnetic moments, such as occurs in ferro, antiferro- and ferri-magnetic materials, there will be a contribution of magnetic scattering to coherent reflections. In ferromagnetic materials these will appear in the same angular positions as the ordinary chemical or nuclear reflections but in the other cases entirely new reflections may appear in witness of the fact that the magnetic unit cell may be larger, along one or more of its axes, than the ordinary chemical crystallographic unit cell. It is the study of these new additional reflections which enables neutron diffraction to study magnetism on an atomic scale, leading to information on the location, orientation and magnitude of the magnetic moments in these materials.

It has been noted that the value of p can be calculated if the electronic structure of an atom or ion is known. This is in contrast to the nuclear scattering amplitude b which cannot be calculated from our present knowledge of nuclear structure. The expression for p in eqn. (1) refers to the simplest case in which the magnetic moment of an atom or ion is due to spin only. This is largely true for most of the ions or metals of the $3d$ transition group in which the *orbital* moments of the ions are wholly or partially quenched by the crystalline field, which exists as a consequence of the regular arrangement of atoms in a solid. This does not happen however for compounds of the rare-earth metals, and for these it is found, both from the neutron scattering and from measurements of magnetic susceptibility, that the magnetic moment is practically the same as would be expected for the free ion. Thus the orbital contribution to the magnetic moment is fully effective. In these cases we have to replace $2S$ in (1) by the more general expression for the effective magnetic moment, which we can write as gJ where the quantum number J expresses the total angular momentum and g is the Landé splitting factor (see Refs. 4, 8, 9). The greater complication is that the form factor "f" will have different values, at a given scattering angle, for the spin and orbital contributions to the magnetic moment. This more general case has been discussed by Trammell.[10] We refer to it here because, as we shall see later, measurements of the paramagnetic scattering of certain rare-earth carbides have been used to draw deductions about the electronic state of the rare-earth ions in these compounds.

1.6. Experimental Techniques

The principles which govern the collection of experimental data with neutrons are similar to those which apply with X-rays, but the details are different and the relative importance of particular factors is different in the two cases. First of all, we mention that an X-ray diffraction tube emits intense almost monochromatic radiation, having a wavelength characteristic of the emitting cathode, superimposed on a background of "white" radiation, but the neutron beam from a reactor is entirely "white", that is, it has a continuous smooth spectrum. The two cases are contrasted in Fig. 1.4 and it is necessary to separate out

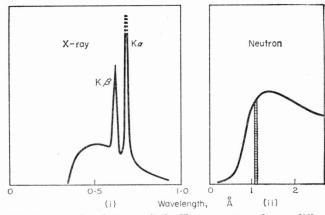

FIG. 1.4. A comparison between (i) the X-ray spectrum from a diffraction tube and (ii) the neutron spectrum from an atomic reactor. A narrow band of wavelength is selected from the neutron spectrum by a monochromator, as marked in curve (ii).

from the neutron spectrum a narrow band of wavelength as indicated in Fig. 1.4 (ii). This is done by first channelling a beam of neutrons from the reactor by means of a collimator which ensures that only those travelling normal to the reactor face, to within half-a-degree or so, are used: the beam is then reflected from the face of a large single crystal, usually of copper or lead, and the reflected neutrons will all have wavelengths close to a constant value λ determined by the angular setting of this crystal. The value of λ can be calculated by the Bragg equation $\lambda = 2d \sin \theta$, where d is the interplanar spacing for the reflecting planes in the crystal and θ is the glancing angle which the incident beams makes with them. Usually a wavelength between 1 and 1·1 Å is used. It might have been expected from Fig. 1.4 (ii) that a wavelength closer to the peak of the spectrum (say 1·5 Å) would have been chosen, in order to get a higher intensity in the reflected beam. However, as well as reflecting a wavelength λ the monochomating crystal also reflects a component of $\lambda/2$ and it will be appreciated that for $\lambda = 1·5$ Å this " second order " component at $\lambda = 0·75$ Å would be sufficiently intense to be very troublesome. If, however, λ is chosen at about 1·05 Å then the second order component is weak enough to be entirely neglected for most purposes: in practice its intensity amounts to only about one-third of one per cent of that of the primary wavelength.

The monochromatic beam of neutrons produced in this way is then allowed to fall on the sample under examination, which is mounted on the axis of a spectrometer, about which a neutron detector rotates and enables a measurement to be made of the variation of the diffracted-beam intensity, as the scattering angle 2θ changes. Figure 1.5 is a diagrammatic sketch of an assembly for doing neutron-diffraction measurements at a nuclear reactor. The scale on the diagram indicates the large size of the apparatus, compared with the much smaller size of a normal X-ray diffractometer which is commonly used for detecting the scattered X-rays from a single-crystal or powdered sample: an X-ray *camera* using photographic film as the detector will be much smaller still. The reason for the much larger apparatus which is needed for neutrons is that the intensity of a neutron beam, measured in terms of quanta $cm^{-2} sec^{-1}$, is very much lower than for X-rays. As a consequence a large sample and a large beam have to be used. With high-flux reactors, which have been coming into use since about 1958 and in which the peak neutron flux is a few times 10^{13} neutrons $cm^{-2} sec^{-1}$, a single-crystal which measures 2–3 mm in each direction is about the right size for study, but a sample in polycrystalline form would need to be much larger and a cylinder of height about 2 cm and diameter 4 mm is generally used. In order to irradiate samples of this size it is necessary to have an incident beam with an area of two or three square centimetres. With reactors which give a lower neutron flux even larger beams are needed if polycrystalline or powdered material is to be studied and in this case samples with a volume of about 5 cm^3 may be needed.

The large samples which are often needed for neutron diffraction, in order to give adequately intense diffracted beams, impose a limitation on the angular resolution which can be achieved. Especially with powder samples the geometry of the apparatus has to be chosen to give a compromise between high intensity and good angular resolution. The detecting counter is usually placed 40 cm or more from the diffracting sample and Soller type collimators may be placed between the two in order to give improved angular resolution. Up to the present time counters filled with gaseous boron trifluoride, BF_3 made from the B^{10} isotope, have been used almost exclusively as detectors, in spite of their large size. With single-crystal samples a counter 15 cm in length and either 1 or 2 in. in diameter is generally used but for polycrystalline samples, where the diffracted intensities are much weaker, a counter of length 60 cm is commonly used in order to get a detection efficiency of about 70 per

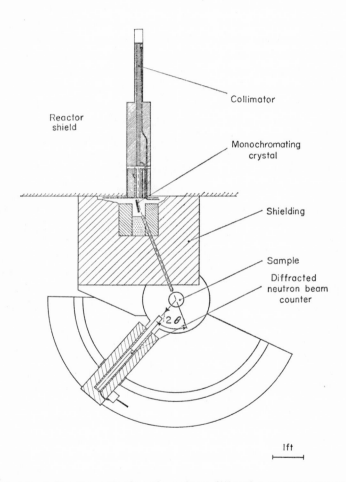

Reactor shield

Collimator

Monochromating crystal

Shielding

Sample

Diffracted neutron beam counter

2θ

lft

FIG. 1.5. A diagrammatic plan of a neutron-diffraction spectrometer at a nuclear reactor. The detecting counter rotates around the axis of the instrument, on which the sample is mounted, and the diffracted intensity is measured as a function of 2θ, the angle of scattering.

cent when working with a wavelength of 1 Å. In either case the counter has to be surrounded in all directions by 10 cm or so of shielding material, in order to screen the counter from stray neutrons which would produce a high and often variable background, so that the resulting counter assembly is both large and heavy. It is mainly the cumbersome counter, particularly when this has to be placed at a substantial distance from the sample, which accounts for the large size of conventional neutron spectrometers and the substantial form of their construction. Development work continues on smaller types of counter, such as both crystal and liquid scintillators and photographic methods of detection, but these have not yet been shown to have such good characteristics as the BF$_3$ counter. Very encouraging progress has recently been made in photographic methods of detection. By using scintillating screens composed of Li^{6}F and ZnS, together with high-speed Polaroid film, both Smith[11] of Oak Ridge and Shull and his colleagues[12] at M.I.T. Cambridge, U.S.A., have achieved improvements in sensitivity by ten or more times compared with earlier attempts. Apart from its potential use in actually recording diffraction patterns this photographic method is extremely valuable in the preparatory work of aligning the diffraction spectrometer and adjusting the sample crystals.

It will have been realized from the previous paragraphs that the details of the experimental apparatus and arrangements will depend on whether polycrystalline material or single-crystals are being studied. Single-crystals are almost always used if they can be grown of suitable size. Each reflecting plane of the crystal then has to be oriented and studied separately, with the result that observations are much more lengthy and many precise adjustments have to be made, but the final conclusions from the investigation are vastly more informative. Indeed, for any approach towards a direct deduction of a crystal structure —as distinct from a trial-and-error verification of a suggested model— single-crystal techniques are essential, and this is a general conclusion which applies equally to both X-ray and neutron diffraction studies. In both cases much thought and ingenuity is being devoted to making the process of data-collection largely automatic and this is especially important when the detector is some form of counter, which collects radiation from only a small angular range at any one time, rather than a photographic film which gives continuous cover over the whole angular range of detection. The next few years are likely to see the introduction of more and more automatic equipment, not only for the actual process of collecting the intensity data at the spectrometer but also for processing it to a form in which it can be handled by the electronic computers which work out the atomic parameters of the crystal structure by Fourier synthesis or least-squares analysis. At the present time, however, most neutron-diffraction apparatus is only automatic to the extent that it will continue to collect data over periods of 24 hours or so without intermediate attention. A variety of methods is in use in different laboratories for the actual display of the diffraction pattern. Typical examples are a continuous visual plot of diffracted intensity versus scattering angle, secured by a steadily and continuously rotating counter which is connected through a ratemeter to a pen recorder, or a counter which moves discontinuously in small angular steps, of a fraction of a degree, and then prints on to a paper tape the total neutron count which has been accumulated at each angular position.

Before concluding this brief summary of the experimental techniques used in neutron-diffraction measurements it may be valuable to make a few comments on the absorption coefficients of materials for neutrons, since these may determine whether or not certain materials can be examined. In general the absorption coefficients of elements for neutrons with a wavelength of about 1 Å are very small.[4] Typical values of the linear absorption coefficients μ of solid elements are 0·19 cm^{-1} for copper and 0·01 cm^{-1} for tin: these values can be contrasted with the corresponding values for Cu$K\alpha$ X-rays, which are 470 and 1540 cm^{-1} respectively. It is fortunate that the absorption is usually so low, since otherwise it would not be possible to attain reasonable intensities by making use of quite large samples. There are, however, certain elements which have exceptionally large absorption coefficients for neutrons, such as cadmium for which μ is about 100 and some of the rare-earth elements—e.g. samarium and gadolinium—which have even larger values. Accordingly, polycrystalline samples which contain these elements may be difficult to study.

A consequence of the normally low absorption coefficient of materials for neutrons is that when a neutron beam passes through a material its attenuation is very largely due to sideways scattering of the beam rather than to true absorption. This fact is of importance when the intensities of the diffracted spectra from single-crystals are being considered. It can be shown[4] that it results in a good deal more of what is known as "secondary extinction" than is met with in X-ray diffraction. The consequence of this is that there may be a departure from the normal linear relation between intensity and F^2, i.e. the square of the "structure amplitude factor" which we have discussed earlier in this chapter. This sets a limit on the maximum size of crystal which can conveniently be used for crystal structure analysis, unless a lot of difficult corrections are made. In practice it is found that when rather large crystals are needed with reactors of low neutron intensity then quite substantial corrections need to be estimated for the most intense of the reflections. Fortunately the difficulty becomes much less troublesome for the smaller crystals which give adequate intensities with high-flux reactors: corrections may, however, still be very important if the crystal texture is highly perfect.

From the practical point of view the low absorption coefficients of most materials for neutrons simplify the problems which are involved in the construction of apparatus for making measurements at high or low temperatures. This is of importance in many applications: for example, it may be necessary to study some material which melts below room temperature or it may be desirable to reduce the temperature in order to lessen the thermal motion of the molecules. Equally it may be desired to observe phase changes at elevated temperatures. In either case the neutron beam is very little impaired by, say, the thin aluminium walls of a low-temperature cryostat or the copper holder of a simple furnace for high-temperature measurements. With the relatively large samples of material which are used it also becomes a fairly simple matter to measure directly the temperature of the sample, using a thermocouple placed in direct contact with it.

1.7. Inelastic Scattering

In recent years the techniques of "inelastic" neutron scattering[4] have been applied to chemical problems. When a neutron passes through a solid it may lose or gain energy by exciting, or de-exciting, vibrations in the solid. A study of the energy changes which take place will reveal details of the spectrum of these vibrations.

Two experimental methods have been used so far. In the first, reported by Woods et al.[13] and by Venkataraman et al.,[14] vibrations are excited in the solid, so that higher-energy neutrons lose some of their energy. In the second method, employed by Palevsky,[15] very low energy neutrons take up energy from the solid.

It seems likely that these techniques will yield important information as they become further developed.

REFERENCES

1. BRAGG, W. L. *The Crystalline State*, vol. 1, Bell, London, 1949.
   LIPSON, H. and COCHRAN, W. *The Crystalline State*, vol. 3, Bell, London, 1957.
   BUERGER, M. J. *Crystal Structure Analysis*, Wiley, New York, 1960.
2. HALBAN, H. and PREISWORK, P. *C. R. Acad. Sci. Paris*, 1936, **203**, 73.
3. MITCHELL, D. P. and POWERS, P. N. *Phys. Rev.*, 1936, **50**, 486.
4. BACON, G. E. *Neutron Diffraction*, 2nd ed., Oxford University Press, London, 1962.
   This gives a comprehensive account of the general principles and applications of neutron diffraction with references to most of the original papers. Chapter II gives an account of the process by which atoms scatter neutrons and the significance of such factors as "resonance" and "potential" scattering, spin- and isotope-incoherence. Chapter VII describes "inelastic" scattering.
5. CURTISS, L. F. *Introduction to Neutron Physics*, Van Nostrand, Princeton, N.J., U.S.A., 1959.
   See in particular, Chapter II, *Particle and Nuclear Interactions* and Chapter VI, *Interactions of Neutrons with Matter*.
6. HALLIDAY, D. *Introductory Nuclear Physics*, Wiley, New York, 1950.
   See Chapter 6: *Neutrons—Production, Detection and Interaction with Matter*.
7. HUGHES, D. J. *Neutron Cross Sections*, Pergamon Press, London, 1957.
   This is a guide to the use and interpretation of standard compilations of nuclear data, and Chapters 1, 2, 4 and 6 will be found of particular interest.
8. VAN VLECK, J. H. *The Theory of Electric and Magnetic Susceptibilities*, Oxford University Press, London, 1931.
9. BATES, L. F. *Modern Magnetism*, 3rd ed., Cambridge University Press, 1951.
10. TRAMMELL, G. T. *Phys. Rev.* 1953, **92**, 1387.
11. SMITH, H. G. *Rev. sci. Instrum.*, 1962, **33**, 128.
12. WANG, S. P., SHULL, C. G. and PHILLIPS, W. C. *Rev. sci. Instrum.* 1962, **33**, 126.
13. WOODS, A. D. B., *et al.* Symposium on Inelastic Scattering of Neutrons, 1961, Vienna, I.A.E.A., p. 487.
14. VENKATARAMAN, G., *et al.* Symposium on Inelastic Scattering of Neutrons, Chalk River, Canada, 1962.
15. PALEVSKY, H. *J. Phys. Soc. Japan.*, 1962, **17**, Suppl. B-II, 367.

CHAPTER 2

HYDROGEN BONDS IN INORGANIC COMPOUNDS

2.1. Introduction: KHF_2 and KH_2PO_4

In discussing the early contributions of neutron diffraction to this subject we shall need to emphasize one or two technical points in order to give the reader some idea of the factors which limit the scope and accuracy of the technique. Later on we shall largely confine ourselves to the results of the investigations and to pointing out such general conclusions as have been established.

The systematic study of hydrogen bonds by neutron diffraction began in 1952 with the analysis of a single crystal of KHF_2 by Peterson and Levy.[1] In this compound the two fluorine atoms are joined by a hydrogen bond which produces the extremely short interatomic separation of 2·26 Å for F—F. The aim of the neutron investigation was to secure direct evidence to favour either a single or a double minimum in the potential between the two atoms: each of these alternative interpretations had been proposed in the past. In the case of a double minimum model there would, most probably, be a random distribution of hydrogen atoms between the two positions either side of the mid-point, equivalent to the placing of a half-atom in each position. Comparison of the neutron data with calculations for various models suggested that the hydrogen atom was centred to an accuracy of about 0·06 Å. The precision, as always in this kind of study, is limited by the relatively large thermal motion of the hydrogen atom which makes the observed intensities less sensitive to small changes in the equilibrium position of the atom. From the technical point of view this study was particularly interesting because the authors also presented their results in the form of a Fourier synthesis of the neutron scattering density, as a projection on the 001 plane. This projection is shown as Fig. 2.1 and, although it was constructed from rather a limited number of terms and therefore shows marked effects due to "series termination", it indicated how this form of presentation would be as useful for neutron data as for X-rays. We draw attention to one point of detail in this projection, namely

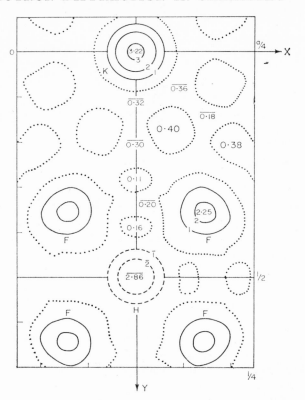

Fig. 2.1. A projection on the 001 plane of the neutron scattering density in KHF₂. Positive contours are shown as full lines: the negative contours of the hydrogen atoms are shown as broken lines and the zero contour is dotted. (After Peterson and Levy, *J. chem. Phys.* 1952, **20**, 704.)

that the contours of the hydrogen atom appear as negative values because of the negative scattering amplitude of ordinary hydrogen which we noted in Chapter 1.

This work was soon followed by much more ambitious investigations of the hydrogen bonds in potassium di-hydrogen phosphate, KH_2PO_4, which were carried out concurrently and independently in England[2, 3] and the U.S.A.[4, 5] A prime aim of the former work, apart from the chemical interest, was to demonstrate in detail the applicability of Fourier synthesis methods to neutron diffraction and to indicate the best methods of presenting the data. The most important point is clearly illustrated in Fig. 2.2 which shows two projections of the structure of KH_2PO_4 at a temperature of $-195°C$ obtained by Bacon and

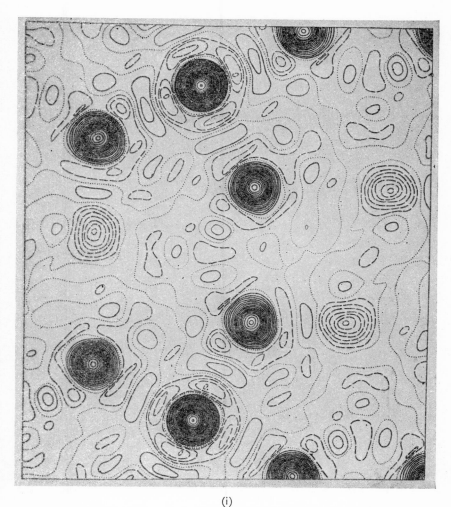

(i)

FIG. 2.2. Neutron diffraction projections on the 001 plane for the ferro-
electric form of KH_2PO_4, from intensity data for single crystals at about
80°K. Diagram (i) shows all the atoms in the structure, the most intense
peaks being those of the superimposed potassium and phosphorus atoms.
Diagram (ii) is a difference projection for which the contributions of the
K, P, O atoms have been subtracted, leaving only hydrogen atoms in the
picture. In each case positive contours are shown by full lines and negative
contours by broken lines.

In order to secure projections of this kind it is necessary to maintain the
whole crystal as a single domain by applying an electric field. When the
direction of the field is reversed the hydrogen atoms move over into
the complementary positions which are indicated by crosses in diagram (ii).
(Bacon and Pease, *Proc. roy. Soc.* A. 1953, **220**, 397 and 1955, **230**, 359.)

(ii)

Pease.[3] The first projection shows all the atoms in the structure and is obtained by making a direct synthesis of F_o, the observed structure amplitude factor: the magnitude of this amplitude, but not its sign, can be obtained from the neutron intensities. The second projection shows only the hydrogen atoms in the structure and was obtained in a manner which we shall describe shortly. At the outset we mention that the apparent diameters of the atoms revealed by these projections are about 1 Å, roughly the same size as atoms appear to X-rays, although the scattering centre for the neutrons is the *nucleus* which has a diameter of only 10^{-12} cm. There are two reasons for the great smearing-out of the nucleus which occurs in the neutron picture. First, the nucleus does not remain in its equilibrium position but vibrates under the influence of thermal energy, with a root–mean square amplitude of about 0·1 Å. Secondly, the accuracy of our picture is limited because we are able to observe only a finite number of spectra and this limits our resolving power in the same way as the accuracy of reproduction of an object in an optical microscope is limited by the size of the aperture. The apparent size of our atoms is the resultant of these two effects. Detailed analysis shows, as in the optical analogy, that the amplitude of an atom in the projection will fall from its peak value to zero and then take a small negative value, passing through a series of diffraction ripples of decreasing amplitude and alternately negative and positive in sign. Some of these can be distinguished in Fig. 2.2(i) in the neighbourhood of heavily scattering atoms. The same effect of diffraction ripples, or the "series termination" effect it is often called, occurs in the case of X-ray diffraction but there is an important difference here which modifies its effect. With X-rays each point of the electron cloud around the atom contributes its own ripples but in the superposition of the patterns, to give a resultant for the whole atom, most of the details are smeared out. An alternative way of looking at the difference is to note that the scattering from a point nucleus is isotropic, i.e. the same for all angles of scattering, whereas the X-ray scattering from an extended cloud of electrons has a "form-factor" which describes the way in which the scattering falls off quite quickly as the angle of scattering is increased.

It will be appreciated that the diffraction ripples around the atoms with large neutron-scattering amplitudes may give spurious effects in our Fourier projections, particularly when they overlap the atomic position of some effectively "lighter" atom in the projection. Indeed such effects account largely for the rather irregular shapes of the hydrogen atoms in Fig. 2.2(i). We can remove these spurious effects from our picture by constructing "difference" projections as in the right-hand projection (ii) of Fig. 2.2. In order to make this projection we carry out a synthesis not of F_o but of $(F_o - F_{KPO})$, where F_{KPO} is the calculated contribution to the structure factor of all the atoms *except* hydrogen. We can make such a calculation at this later stage in the analysis by using the information which we have obtained about the potassium, phosphorus and oxygen atoms not only from the neutron data but also from earlier work with X-rays. The errors in the final projection, apart from experimental errors, will be confined to the effect of diffraction ripples from hydrogen atoms. Such remaining spurious effects will be of very little importance because neighbouring hydrogen atoms are relatively far apart. As can be seen from the right-hand portion of Fig. 2.2 the resultant contours for the hydrogen atoms are very regular in shape.

When the approximate positions of the hydrogen atoms have been determined by Fourier synthesis methods, with the assistance of previous knowledge of the position of other atoms which has been secured by using X-ray diffraction observations, the structure is then "refined" by least-squares analysis. The computation is carried out by electronic machines using programmes which are generally slight modifications of ones designed for handling X-ray diffraction data. We emphasized earlier that there is no entirely *direct* way of deducing a crystal structure from diffraction data because we cannot measure the *phases* of the diffracted spectra. A preliminary guess at the structure has first to be made using general knowledge of the chemical and physical properties and the crystal morphology of the compound which is under investigation and also by taking into account established information about atomic sizes. By trial and error a structure is evolved which gives rough agreement with the observed diffraction intensities and which, in turn, then serves for making a calculation of the signs (or phases) of the structure amplitudes. In this way the X-ray crystallographer arrives at an approximate structure which he then generally proceeds to refine by least-squares analysis. This knowledge is almost always available to the neutron crystallographer at the outset, so that the latter's task is usually to continue the process of refinement by taking due account of the hydrogen atoms, which will have been ignored, or will have been very insignificant, in considering the X-ray diffraction data. In most cases it is found that the hydrogen atom positions can be guessed sufficiently accurately to reduce to a very small number the spectra for which the signs of the observed structure amplitude factors are uncertain.

Returning to the conclusions which can be drawn from the neutron study of KH_2PO_4 we point out that Fig. 2.2 demonstrates in very direct fashion the truth of Slater's[6] hypothesis that below the transition temperature to the ferro-electric state there is an ordered distribution of protons throughout each ferro-electric domain in the crystal. In fact, in order to obtain this projection it was necessary to ensure that the whole of the crystal under observation was a single domain. This was achieved by applying an electric field along the c-axis of the crystal. If the field is reversed in direction then all the protons change their positions, moving over to the complementary set of positions which are marked by crosses in Fig. 2.2(ii). This modification of the synthesized projection is a consequence of some very marked changes in the intensities of the diffracted spectra when the field is reversed. The effect is very striking in certain instances: for example the 400 intensity increases by a factor of ten times and 040 is correspondingly reduced.

The O—O separation in KH_2PO_4 is 2·49 Å and in the ordered state the O—H distance is 1·05 $\pm$ 0·014 Å. Above 132°K the ordering of

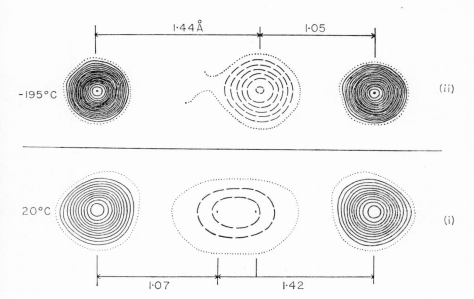

Fig. 2.3. A comparison of the hydrogen bond in KH_2PO_4, above and below the ferroelectric transition temperature. In (i) at room temperature, there is an elongated distribution of scattering density for the hydrogen atom which is probably due to the effective superposition of two half-hydrogen atoms, one on each side of the mid-point of the bond. At (ii), in the ferroelectric state, there is an ordered arrangement of hydrogen atoms producing an unsymmetrical bond for which O—H = 1·05 Å.

the protons is destroyed and the pattern of neutron scattering density between the oxygen atoms changes as illustrated by comparison of the two sections of Fig. 2.3. The distribution which is shown here for room temperature could be interpreted in two different ways, either as a centrally-placed proton with very anisotropic motion, or as a disordered distribution between two possible positions, one on either side of the mid-point between the two oxygen atoms. In view of other physical data the second alternative is the much more likely situation and if Fig. 2.3(i) is then interpreted on this model it is found that the O—H distances are $1 \cdot 07 \pm 0 \cdot 01$ Å, with a separation of $0 \cdot 35$ Å between the two positions.

The room temperature structure of tetragonal $(NH_4)H_2PO_4$ has also been studied[7] and it was found that there is a network of $H_2PO_4^-$ ions very similar to those in the potassium compound. Moreover the lengths of the O—O and O—H distances are very nearly the same for the two compounds. There is an additional interest in the study of the ammonium compound because neutrons can locate accurately the hydrogen atoms in the ammonium group. The ammonium ion appears to be slightly distorted from a regular tetrahedron, with bond angles of $107°31'$ and $113°20'$. The length of the N—H bond is $1 \cdot 00$ Å.

2.2. Ice and Crystalline Hydrates

A study of the hydrogen atoms in ice was first made by Wollan, Davidson and Shull[8] in 1949, when neutron diffraction technique was restricted to the study of polycrystalline material by powder methods. The conclusions of this work were indeed correct but they can be seen much more elegantly in a later study of single crystals by Peterson and Levy.[9] Both studies were actually made with deuterated ice in order to get the most satisfactory diffraction pattern, free from as much unnecessary background scattering as possible. It was already known from X-ray data that ice had a very symmetrical structure in which the oxygen atoms are located at the centres and corners of regular tetrahedra, with an interatomic separation of $2 \cdot 76$ Å for O—O. The neutron projections support the model which was proposed by Pauling[10] in 1935, according to which there is one hydrogen atom on each link between adjacent oxygen atoms, located so that it is closer to one oxygen atom than the other. The apparent effect over the whole crystal, which appears clearly in the projection in Fig. 2.4, is that of placing a half-hydrogen atom at each of the possible positions, but the detailed nature of the type of disorder which leads to this resultant effect is not understood. However, we emphasize that in this case, in contrast to what we found in KH_2PO_4, the distance of separation between the pairs of positions is large enough for the half-hydrogens to be almost completely resolved in the projection of scattering density. This happens because the hydrogen bonds in ice are of the "long"

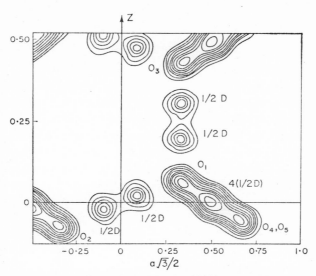

FIG. 2.4. A neutron-diffraction projection of "deuterated" ice on a plane at right-angles to the y-axis of the hexagonal structure. The oxygen atom O_1 is tetrahedrally surrounded by the oxygen atoms O_2, O_3, O_4, and O_5. Atoms O_1, O_2, O_3, lie in the plane of the projection and are joined by hydrogen bonds in the plane. There is a disordered arrangement of deuterium atoms between pairs of possible positions, each marked as $\frac{1}{2}D$, between the oxygen atoms. Note that the deuterium atoms, like oxygen but unlike ordinary hydrogen atoms, have a positive scattering amplitude for neutrons. (After Peterson and Levy, *Acta cryst.* 1957, **10**, 70.)

variety with an O—O separation of 2·76 Å. Moreover, in this longer and weaker bond the O—H distance is considerably shorter than was found in KH_2PO_4. The measured O—H distance, as found for deuterated ice at −50°C, is 1·01 ± ·01 Å which means that the separation between the two half-hydrogen positions is 0·74 Å. The detailed geometry of the tetrahedral environment of an oxygen atom is shown in Fig. 2.5 from which it will be seen that the O—H——O hydrogen bonds are straight within a very small experimental inaccuracy and that both the H—O—H and O—O—O angles are very close to the true tetrahedral angle of 109·6°.

In crystalline hydrates the environment of the oxygen atoms in the water molecules is no longer tetrahedral and it is of some interest to determine how the shape and size of the water molecules differs from that in ice, bearing in mind that in the free water molecule, in gaseous steam, the O—H bond length is 0·96 Å and the bond angle is 104·6°. A variety of inorganic hydrates has now been examined and some of the conclusions are summarized in Table 2.1 in which the angles listed

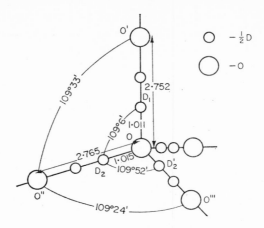

FIG. 2.5. The tetrahedral environment of an oxygen atom in the structure of deuterated ice at $-50°C$. (Peterson and Levy, *Acta cryst.* 1957, **10**, 70.)

TABLE 2.1

Bond angles and thermal parameters in hydrates

Substance	H—O—H		O—O—O	B_H	B_O
D_2O ice. $(-50°C)$		$109 \cdot 1°$	$109 \cdot 5°$	$3 \cdot 2$	$2 \cdot 3$
		$109 \cdot 9°$	$109 \cdot 4°$		
$Na_2CO_3.NaHCO_3.2H_2O$		$107°$	$114°$	$3 \cdot 9$	$2 \cdot 0$
$K_2SO_4.Cr_2(SO_4)_3.24H_2O$	O_K	$103°$	$94°$	$4 \cdot 1$	$2 \cdot 8$
	O_{Cr}	$107°$	$102°$	$3 \cdot 3$	$2 \cdot 5$
$(COOH)_2 \ 2H_2O$		$106°$	$84°$		
$CuCl_2.2H_2O$		$108°$	$97°$ (O—Cl)		
$CaSO_4.2H_2O$		$106°$	$108°$	$3 \cdot 7$	$2 \cdot 4$
$Li_2SO_4.HO_2$		$110°$	$146°$		
$CuSO_4.5H_2O$		$111°$	$121°$	$3 \cdot 5$	$1 \cdot 8$
		$109°$	$130°$	$2 \cdot 8$	$1 \cdot 5$
		$114°$	$119°$	$3 \cdot 0$	$2 \cdot 1$
		$109°$	$105°$	$2 \cdot 9$	$2 \cdot 4$
		$106°$	$122°$	$3 \cdot 2$	$1 \cdot 9$

H—O—H, O—O—O are the angles specified in Fig. 2.6. B_H, B_O are the isotropic Debye factors for the thermal motion of the hydrogen and oxygen atoms in the water molecules, expressed in $(Å)^2$. If the root-mean-square displacement of an atom in any direction is $\bar{u}$ then $80\bar{u}^2 = B$.

are those specified in Fig. 2.6. The first hydrate examined[11] was the mineral "trona", sodium sesquicarbonate $Na_2CO_3.NaHCO_3.2H_2O$, and the projection of the neutron scattering density on the 010 plane is shown in Fig. 2.7. This projection is particularly informative because

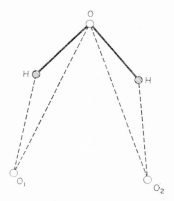

FIG. 2.6. The surroundings of a water-molecule in hydrates. H—O—H is the angle within the water-molecule. The angle O_1—O—O_2 is determined by the positions of the neighbouring oxygen atoms to which O is linked by hydrogen bonds. This O_1—O—O_2 angle is often found to be quite different from the angle H—O—H, resulting in bent hydrogen bonds.

the plane of the water molecules is almost parallel to the plane of the projection. The figure shows very clearly how hydrogen bonds link the carbonate groups together via the intervening water molecules. It is just possible to see from the figure that the hydrogen bonds are slightly bent in order to retain[27] an H—O—H angle of about 108° in spite of the larger O—O—O angle of 114°. The total length of the O—H——O bond is 2·76 Å, which is the same as for the bond in ice, and it will be noted that the O—H distance of 1·01 Å is also the same as for ice within the experimental error. The difference between the two substances is, of course, that in trona there is a completely ordered arrangement of hydrogen atoms to form individual water molecules, whereas in ice there is a disordered arrangement which is equivalent to a distribution of "half-hydrogens" which achieves tetrahedral symmetry. A more extreme example[12] of bent hydrogen bonds is provided by potassium chromium alum $K_2SO_4\ Cr_2(SO_4)_3.24\ H_2O$, in which six water molecules surround each of the potassium and chromium atoms. The environment in the two cases is shown in Fig. 2.8: in each case the O—O—O angle is considerably smaller than the tetrahedral angle but, at the expense of bent hydrogen bonds, the water molecules resist very largely any

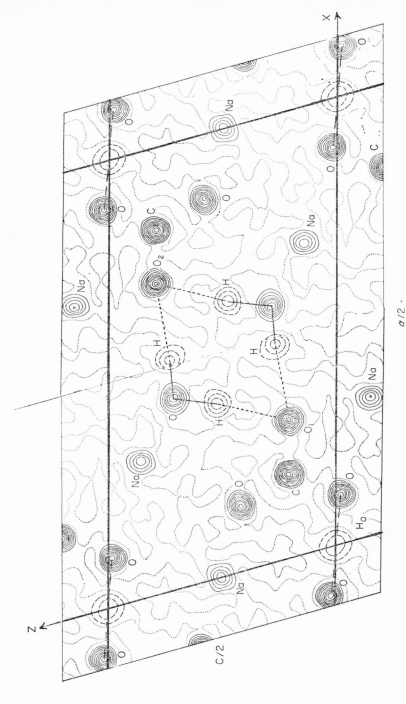

Fig. 2.7. A projection of the neutron scattering density of Na_2CO_3, $NaHCO_3.2H_2O$ showing the form of the molecules of water of crystallization and indicating the hydrogen bonds which bind the structure together. (Bacon and Curry, *Acta cryst.* 1956, **9**, 82.)

tendency for this environment to reduce the H—O—H angle. The opposite tendency is resisted equally well in the case of $CuSO_4.5H_2O$ where the average value[13] of the five O—O—O angles is 120°. One of the hydrogen bonds is bent by 26° in order to accommodate these large angles and, at the same time, retain an angle close to 109° within the water molecules. Another very recent example of a study of a hydrate which has revealed very bent hydrogen bonds is $Li_2SO_4.H_2O$ which has been examined by Smith, Peterson and Levy.[14] The single water molecule in each formula group is linked by two very weak bonds to, first, an

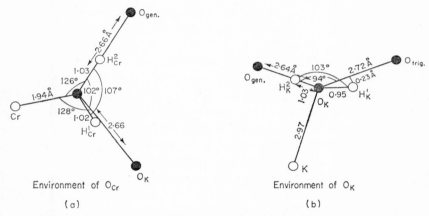

FIG. 2.8. The shape and environment of the water molecules in potassium chromium alum (a) around a chromium atom and (b) around a potassium atom. (Bacon and Gardner, *Proc. roy. Soc.* A. 1958, **246**, 78.)

equivalent water molecule (at 2·95 Å) and, secondly, to an oxygen atom in a sulphate group. The lengths of these two bonds are 2·95, 2·86 Å respectively and they are both bent by about 30°.

In each of the hydrates which we have discussed the hydrogen bond is between two oxygen atoms but in $CuCl_2.2H_2O$ there is[15] a very weak hydrogen bond of length about 3·2 Å between a chlorine ion and an oxygen atom of a water molecule. The dimensions of the water molecule are very close to those found in steam.

It will be appreciated that hydrates are usually easy to grow in large crystals and that they were, accordingly, very convenient subjects for study with what would today be regarded as low-flux reactors. All the examples which we have been discussing were examined with reactors giving a flux of about 2×10^{12} neutrons cm^{-2} sec^{-1}. The general accuracy of the measurements is probably best appreciated by referring back to Table 2.1 which indicates not only the constancy of the angle H—O—H but also fairly constant values of the Debye factors which measure the thermal motion of the hydrogen and oxygen atoms in the water molecules of the various hydrates.

2.3. Inorganic Hydroxides

A very thorough study of the mineral diaspore AlO(OH) has been made by Busing and Levy[16] following several X-ray investigations. The resulting structure, which has orthorhombic symmetry, is shown diagrammatically in Fig. 2.9 which represents a projection of the unit cell on the xy plane. The symmetry is such that all the atoms lie on one or other of two mirror planes at $z = \frac{1}{4}$ and $z = -\frac{1}{4}$ and the two sets of atoms are drawn with heavy and light lines respectively in the figure. The most interesting feature of the structure is the position of the hydrogen atom which is between the two crystallographically different oxygen atoms O_I and O_{II}, but considerably closer to O_{II}, so that the bond length O_{II}—H is only 0·990, a little less than that in ice, whereas the distance from H to O_I is 1·694 Å. Moreover the hydrogen atom is displaced from the line joining O_I, O_{II} by about 0·2 Å. A full analysis was made of the thermal motion of all the atoms by using the method of least-squares analysis to give anisotropic temperature factors. The conclusions are represented in Fig. 2.10 which shows the directions of the principal axes of the thermal-motion ellipsoids in the xy plane and it will be noticed that there is particularly large thermal motion for the hydrogen atoms, with a maximum root–mean-square amplitude of 0·146 Å compared with 0·07 Å for the other atoms. It is likely that the resultant thermal motion of the hydrogen atom depends on the motion of O_{II} but not O_I and is in fact compounded of its own random motion superimposed on the movement of O_{II}. In such a case there will be an appreciable average angle of inclination α of the vector O—H relative to its equilibrium position, as indicated in the figure. As a result there is a shortening, pH, of the apparent bond length because the centre of gravity of the thermal distribution does not coincide with the equilibrium position. This is exactly the same effect as that which Cox, Cruickshank and Smith first discussed[17] for the apparent shortening of the C—C bonds in benzene, where they showed that when the motion of an atom is along the arc of a circle its time-averaged distribution will be displaced towards the centre of the circle. In the case of AlO(OH) it is estimated that the apparent O_{II}—H distance of 0·990 Å corresponds

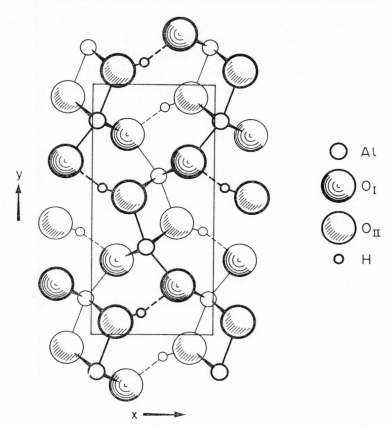

FIG. 2.9. A diagrammatic sketch of the crystal structure of diaspore AlO(OH) as seen when projected on the 001 plane. All the atoms lie in one or other of two planes, (i) at $z = \frac{1}{4}$, above the projection plane and indicated by heavy lines and (ii) at $z = -\frac{1}{4}$, below the plane, and indicated by light lines. There are two crystallographically-different types of oxygen atoms, which are distinguished by the two types of shading as indicated. (Busing and Levy, *Acta cryst.* 1958, **11**, 798.)

to an equilibrium distance of 1·005 Å. A rather smaller correction was indeed also made by Peterson and Levy in their study[9] of ice where a similar assessment of anisotropic thermal motion was made. In each case the high overall precision of the coordinates and thermal parameters can be judged by the fact that the conventional "discrepancy factor" lay between 3 and 4 per cent. This discrepancy factor (which is often given the misnomer of "reliability index") is defined as $\sum |F_o - F_c|/\sum |F_o|$, where F_o is the observed structure–amplitude factor of a reflection, and F_c is the calculated value based on the final model

given by the least-squares analysis. It serves as an overall guide to the
accuracy with which a set of intensity measurements are in agreement
with the calculated predictions from a postulated model.

The structure found in AlO(OH), where there is a hydrogen bond
linking the hydroxyl group to the other oxygen atom, is to be contrasted
with that which was found[18] in calcium hydroxide. The crystals of

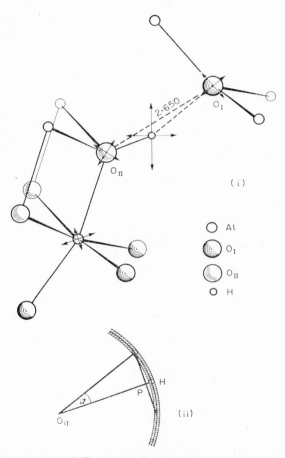

FIG. 2.10. A diagram (i) illustrating the thermal motion in AlO(OH). The
vectors show the principal axes of the thermal motion ellipsoids in the xy
plane and are drawn with lengths equal to the r.m.s. displacements on a
scale five times that of the interatomic distances. The third axis, in the
z-direction, is not shown. Because of the large thermal motion of H its
apparent position is displaced to P, away from its equilibrium position, as
shown at (ii). The equilibrium length for the bond O—H is estimated to be
0·015 Å greater than the apparent value. (After Busing and Levy, *Acta
cryst.* 1958, **11**, 798.)

Ca(OH)₂ have hexagonal symmetry and some of the details of the structure found from a study with neutrons are indicated in Fig. 2.11. As shown in the upper portion (i) of the figure, the oxygen and hydrogen atoms lie in the $11\bar{2}0$ plane and a detailed section through all the atoms in this plane is given in the lower section (ii) of the figure; the thermal motion of the nuclei is indicated by the lengths of the axes of the ellipsoids which have been drawn around the positions of the nuclei. This structure confirms the original suggestion of Bernal and

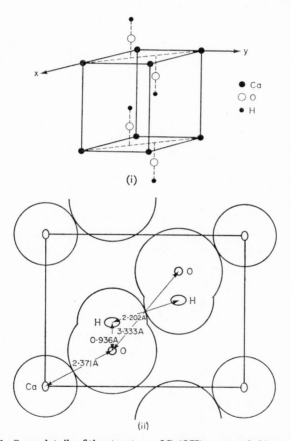

FIG. 2.11. Some details of the structure of Ca(OH)₂ as revealed by neutrons. Diagram (i) shows one unit cell of the hexagonal structure with the O and H atoms lying in the $11\bar{2}0$ plane. Diagram (ii) is a section of the unit cell by this plane, with the nuclei represented by ellipses whose axes are proportional to the root–mean-square thermal motion at room-temperature. The interatomic distances at room temperature are also marked: the O—H distance shown is *before* correction for apparent shortening due to the thermal motion. (After Busing and Levy, *J. chem. Phys.* 1957, **26**, 563.)

Megaw[19] that the large O—O separation of 3·3 Å was too great to allow any possibility of hydrogen bonding. As Fig. 2.11(ii) shows, the structure is noteworthy for the very anisotropic motion of the hydrogen atom, which has a very large motion parallel to the x axis corresponding to Debye B factors of 4·23, 3·31 $\times$ 10^{-16} cm^2 at 20° and $-140°C$ respectively. The full list of thermal parameters is given in Table 2.2.

TABLE 2.2

Thermal motion parameters for $Ca(OH)_2$ at 20° and $-140°C$

Atom	Parameter	20°C	$-140°C$
Ca	B_x	0·70 ± 0·07 Å^2	0·30 ± 0·04 Å^2
Ca	B_z	1·25 ± 0·09 Å^2	0·62 ± 0·05 Å^2
O	B_x	0·73 ± 0·05 Å^2	0·39 ± 0·03 Å^2
O	B_z	0·93 ± 0·05 Å^2	0·52 ± 0·03 Å^2
H	B_x	4·23 ± 0·14 Å^2	3·31 ± 0·08 Å^2
H	B_z	1·34 ± 0·10 Å^2	0·82 ± 0·06 Å^2

The large thermal motion of the hydrogen atom at right-angles to the O—H bond means that there will be an appreciable error (of the type discussed above) in the bond length. The magnitude of the correction will be greater at room temperature, where the thermal motion is larger, and it is interesting to note that although the *apparent* O—H bond length increases from 0·936 Å to 0·944 Å in cooling from 20°C to $-140°C$ nevertheless the corrected bond length is 0·982 Å in each case. Returning to the other bond lengths marked in Fig. 2.11 it is noteworthy that the H—H separation of 2·2 Å is quite close to twice the van der Waals' radius for hydrogen, i.e. the interatomic separation of hydrogen atoms in neighbouring non-bonded molecules found, for example, in organic compounds. Moreover, when the normal ionic radius of 0·99 Å for Ca^{++} is subtracted from the Ca—O distance we are left with 1·38 Å which is very close to the value of 1·40 for the O^{2-} ion. Thus the OH ion appears to behave as an oxide ion in its contact with the Ca^{2+} ion but as a neutral atom of hydrogen at its opposite extremity where it is in contact with the neighbouring OH ion.

A similar absence of hydrogen bonds is reported[20] in lanthanum hydroxide, $La(OH)_3$. Unfortunately this hydroxide could only be studied in powder form and in order to make the analysis practicable, Atoji and Williams studied the deuterated compound $La(OD)_3$, for which the background scattering is considerably reduced compared with that for the ordinary hydrogen compound. The restricted amount of information obtainable from a powder means that only a trial-and-error process, applied to various models, is possible. A plan of the final structure appears in Fig. 2.12 and it is to be noted that all the atoms lie

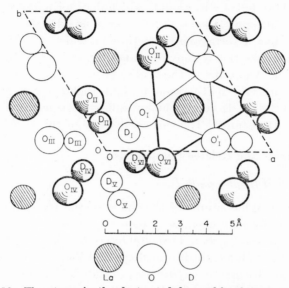

FIG. 2.12. The atoms in the deuterated form of lanthanum hydroxide $La(OD)_3$, projected on the basal plane of the hexagonal unit cell. The atoms lie in parallel planes at $z = \pm\frac{1}{4}$ above and below the plane of projection. Those at $+\frac{1}{4}$ are shown lightly: those at $-\frac{1}{4}$ (or at $z = \frac{3}{4}$ in the cell above) are heavily outlined. (Atoji and Williams, *J. chem. Phys.* 1959, **31**, 329.)

either in the plane $z = \frac{1}{4}$ or at $z = -\frac{1}{4}$ (or $z = \frac{3}{4}$). Within the OD ions there is a short distance, such as O_I—D_I, equal to 0·94 Å but so far as its contacts with other atoms are concerned the deuterium atom behaves as a neutral atom. Thus, around D_I at $z = \frac{1}{4}$ are packed, in square formation, four oxygen atoms—namely O_{II}, O_{VI} at $z = \frac{3}{4}$ and their counterparts O_{II} and O_{VI} at $z = -\frac{1}{4}$ in the unit cell below. The O—D distances for these pairs of atoms are D_I—$O_{V\bar{I}}$ 2·63 and D_I—O_{II} 2·84 Å, and these distances are close to the sum of the van der Waals' radii for deuterium and oxygen. The distances D_I—D_{II} and D_I—D_{III} are 2·32, 2·25 Å respectively, which are roughly twice the van der Waals' radius for hydrogen and very similar to the distances which were found in $Ca(OH)_2$, which we have discussed above.

The distinction between the structures of $AlO(OH)$ on the one hand

and $Ca(OH)_2$ and $La(OD)_3$ on the other would seem to depend on the different abilities of the Al^{3+}, Ca^{2+} and La^{3+} ions to polarize the $(OH)^-$ ion. In the former case strong polarization takes place and the O and H atoms in neighbouring hydroxide ions get close enough together to permit hydrogen bonds to be formed.

A further example of a hydroxide which does form hydrogen bonds is provided by lithium. Dachs (1959) has studied[21] single crystals of LiOH which has a tetragonal structure in which the hydrogen and oxygen atoms are vertically above one another, separated by an apparent distance of $0·92$ Å parallel to the c-axis. However, the hydrogen atoms have a very large thermal motion at right-angles to this axis, i.e. perpendicular to the O—H bond, which results in a large apparent shortening of the O—H distance. The corrected value of this is $0·98 \pm 0·01$ Å.

2.4. Some Acids and Related Compounds

Phosphite and Hypophosphite Ions

Loopstra (1958) has studied[22] the shape of the phosphite and hypophosphite ions by making measurements of neutron-diffraction intensities for phosphorous acid and calcium hypophosphite. In each case the ion is approximately tetrahedral in shape and there are respectively one and two chemically inactive hydrogen atoms linked directly to the phosphorus atom. A projection of calcium hypophosphite as seen along the monoclinic b axis is shown in Fig. 2.13 on which are marked the bond lengths from the phosphorus atom to the surrounding oxygen and hydrogen atoms. The extended structure is made clear in Fig. 2.14: it is a layer structure with the layers running perpendicular to the figure and parallel to 100 which is the cleavage plane. Layers of calcium atoms are covered on both sides with the oxygen atoms of the hypophosphite groups, followed by the phosphorus atoms and the hydrogen atoms which form the outer covering of the composite layers. The distances between the neighbouring hydrogen atoms of different layer-sandwiches, such as the distances $(H_{22}—H_{23})$ and $(H_{11}—H_{14})$, are $2·35$ and $2·45$ Å. The forces between neighbouring sandwiches are therefore of the ordinary van der Waals' type.

The results for phosphorous acid H_3PO_3 show that the structural formula is $HPO(OH)_2$ and that the $(HPO_3)^{2-}$ ion is a deformed tetrahedron. The molecules are held together by hydrogen bonds in such a way that each free oxygen atom accepts two hydrogen bonds from OH groups in neighbouring molecules. The mean O—H——O distance is

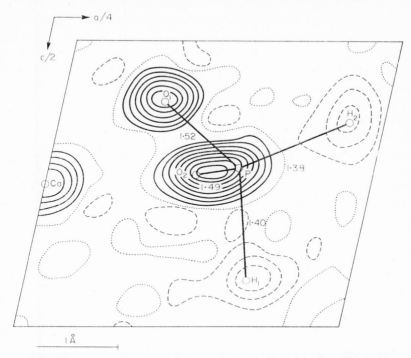

FIG. 2.13. A projection of the neutron scattering density in $Ca(H_2PO_2)_2$ on the 010 plane, showing the dimensions of the hypophosphite ion. Positive contours are full lines, negative contours are broken lines and the zero contours are dotted. (Loopstra, 1958, Ref. 22.)

2·56 Å, which indicates quite a strong bond, but the O—H distances are surprisingly short, all four of them being between 0·96 and 0·98 Å.

$HCrO_2$, $DCrO_2$

Hamilton and Ibers[23] have studied $HCrO_2$ and $DCrO_2$ which contain a short hydrogen bond, measuring about 2·5 Å in each case. This is a short enough distance to suggest that a symmetrical bond might be quite possible. These two acids have a very simple trigonal structure, containing one molecule in the unit cell, and measurements of the powder diffraction pattern were found sufficient for drawing some very important conclusions. The structure is illustrated in Fig. 2.15 and is built up of sandwiches of chromium atoms between sheets of close-packed oxygen atoms. The O—Cr—O sandwiches are stacked normal to the [111] axis and linked together by hydrogen bonds parallel to this axis. For the deuterium compound, it was concluded that the hydrogen bond was almost certainly unsymmetrical: indeed statistical tests led to the

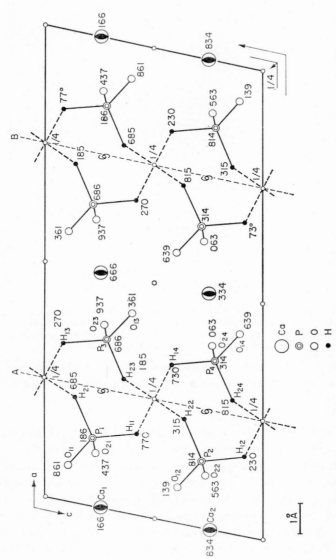

FIG. 2.14. A sketch of the extended structure of Ca(H₂PO₂)₂ as seen along the b-axis of the monoclinic unit cell. Layers of calcium atoms are covered on each side by a sheet of hypophosphite groups, so that the hydrogen atoms lie on the outside of the resulting "sandwich". Successive sandwiches are bonded together (across the planes A, B) purely by van der Waals' forces between the hydrogen atoms which lie at distances of about 2·4 Å apart. (Loopstra, Ref. 22.)

conclusion that the probability that the observed neutron intensity data could be produced by a centred model was only 0·5 per cent. The accuracy which could be obtained with the hydrogen compound is lower, because of the large incoherent background in the powder pattern, but it appeared that the bond in this case was centred, particularly as the thermal motion at right angles to the bond was considerably greater than the component along the bond. These results are in agreement with the infra-red study.

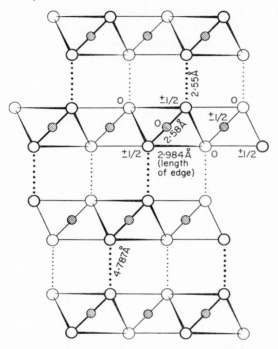

FIG. 2.15. The structure of $HCrO_2$ projected on the $10\bar{1}$ plane. The large circles are oxygen atoms and the small, shaded circles are chromium. Lightly drawn circles are in the plane of the paper and heavy circles indicate ions which are one-half of a repeat distance above and below the paper. Hydrogen bonds, between pairs of oxygen atoms are indicated by dotted lines but the hydrogen atoms themselves are not drawn. (After Douglass, *Acta cryst.* 1957, **10**, 423.)

Iodic Acid

Iodic acid, HIO_3, has been studied by Garrett[24] who followed up the X-ray work of Rogers and Helmholz[25] which had shown that a main characteristic of the structure was the existence of irregular IO_3 pyramids. The outstanding problem was to discover the way in which these pyramids were linked together by the hydrogen atoms. The neutron-diffraction analysis showed that the links are simple unsymmetrical hydrogen bonds with an O—H length of 0·99 Å and an overall O—O separation of 2·69 Å. The suggestion of Rogers and Helmholz that there was a bifurcated hydrogen bond which involved one near-by oxygen and *two* more distant oxygen atoms was clearly disproved. The structure is described best in terms of chains of almost planar pentagonal rings, each sharing one of their sides. Two views of this chain are shown in Fig. 2.16 and it will be seen that the complete hydrogen bond, i.e. O—H——O, forms one side of the pentagon. An oxygen atom O_3 projects alternately above and below the plane of the rings as the molecule is repeated along the chain by the operation of the two-fold screw axis: this is made clear in the lower section of the figure.

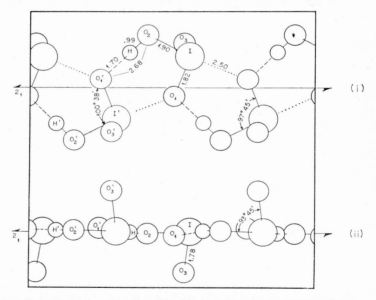

FIG. 2.16. Two views of the chain of pentagonal rings in α-iodic acid. The upper diagram, (i), is a view in a direction at right-angles to the plane of the rings: view (ii) is seen looking along the plane of the rings so that the oxygen atoms O_3, O_3' lie alternately above and below the chain. (Garrett, Ref. 24.)

2.5. The Relation Between O—H and O—H——O Distances

It will have been noticed in the discussion of bond lengths in this chapter that as the overall distance between the oxygen atoms which take part in the hydrogen bond *decreases* there is an *increase* in the O—H distance. For example, for the short bond of 2·49 Å in the ferro-electric form of KH_2PO_4 there is a relatively large O—H distance of 1·05 Å but this has been reduced to 1·01 Å when we come to the longer bond of 2·76 Å which occurs in ice and sodium sesquicarbonate. Some theoretical reasons have been advanced for a simple relationship between the O—H and O—H——O distances but such measurements as have

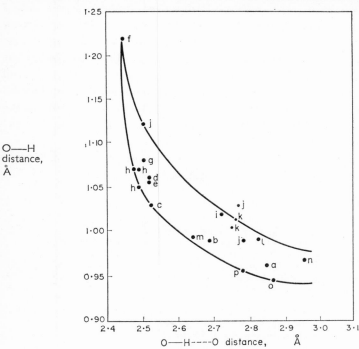

O—H
distance,
Å

O—H----O distance,   Å

FIG. 2.17. A diagram showing the correlation between the O—O and O—H distances in O—H——O hydrogen bonds. The points correspond to (a) $(COOH)_2.2H_2O$ (b) α-HIO_3 (c) KD_2AsO_4 (d) KH_2AsO_4 (e) $(COOH)_2.2H_2O$ (f) nickel dimethyl-glyoxime (g), (h) KH_2PO_4 (i) α-resorcinol (j) $Na_2CO_3.NaHCO_3.2H_2O$ (k) ice (l) $CaSO_4.2H_2O$ (m) AlO(OH) (n), (o) $Li_2SO_4.H_2O$ (p) $CuSO_4.5H_2O$-(average). (Based on Atoji and Rundle, *J. chem. Phys.* 1958, **29**, 1306 with additions.)

been made so far do not support the suggestion that there is any very exact correlation between the two. The information available from neutron diffraction measurements up to 1958 was surveyed[26] by Atoji and Rundle, following their study of gypsum $CaSO_4.2H_2O$. These authors concluded that there was no more than a general correlation of the two distances and this conclusion seems to be supported as more data become available. Figure 2.17 is based on Atoji and Rundle's original diagram with the addition of some later points. The diagram includes several organic compounds which contain hydrogen bonds as well as the inorganic compounds which we have been discussing in the present chapter. The experimental accuracies of the determinations are not as high as would be desired and most of the O—H distance measurements have standard deviations of 0·01 or 0·02 Å. Moreover, only some of these distances have been corrected for errors due to large thermal motion and it is indeed difficult to do this precisely without a very detailed knowledge of the modes of thermal motion which exist. As we have seen, corrections as large as 0·04 Å have been applied in the extreme case of AlO(OH). Nevertheless, when note has been taken of these uncertainties it still seems unlikely that there is an exact correlation between O—H and O—H——O distance. It would seem reasonable to suppose that other details of the environment, such as whether the bonds are straight or bent, will exert some influence.

A recent review of bond lengths and distances, with an extensive table of values, has been given by Hamilton.[28]

REFERENCES

1. PETERSON, S. W. and LEVY, H. A.   *J. chem. Phys.* 1952, **20**, 704.
2. BACON, G. E., and PEASE, R. S.   *Proc. roy. Soc.* A. 1953, **220**, 397.
3. BACON, G. E., and PEASE, R. S.   *Proc. roy. Soc.* A. 1955, **230**, 359.
4. PETERSON, S. W., LEVY, H. A. and SIMONSEN, S. H.   *J. chem. Phys.* 1953, **21**, 2084.
5. PETERSON, S. W., LEVY, H. A. and SIMONSEN, S. H.   *Phys. Rev.* 1954, **93**, 1120.
6. SLATER, J. C.   *J. chem. Phys.* 1941, **9**, 16.
7. TENZER, L., FRAZER, B. C. and PEPINSKY, R.   *Acta cryst.* 1958, **11**, 505.
8. WOLLAN, E. O., DAVIDSON, W. L., and SHULL, C. G.   *Phys. Rev.* 1949, **75**, 1348.
9. PETERSON, S. W. and LEVY, H. A.   *Acta cryst.* 1957, **10**, 70.
10. PAULING, L.   *J. Amer. chem. Soc.* 1935, **57**, 2680.
11. BACON, G. E. and CURRY, N. A.   *Acta cryst.* 1956, **9**, 82.
12. BACON, G. E. and GARDNER, W. E.   *Proc. roy. Soc.* A. 1958, **246**, 78.
13. BACON, G. E. and CURRY, N. A.   *Proc. roy. Soc.* A. 1962, **266**, 95.
14. SMITH, H. G., PETERSON, S. W. and LEVY, H. A.   *Abstract Amer. Cryst. Assoc.* 1961.
15. PETERSON, S. W. and LEVY, H. A.   *J. chem. Phys.* 1957, **26**, 220.
16. BUSING, W. R. and LEVY, H. A.   *Acta cryst.* 1958, **11**, 798.
17. COX, E. G., CRUICKSHANK, D. W. J., and SMITH, J. A. S.   *Nature, London* 1955, **175**, 766.
18. BUSING, W. R., and LEVY, H. A.   *J. chem. Phys.* 1957, **26**, 563.
19. BERNAL, J. D. and MEGAW, H. D.   *Proc. roy. Soc.* A. 1935, **151**, 384.
20. ATOJI, M. and WILLIAMS, D. E.   *J. chem. Phys.* 1959, **31**, 329.
21. DACHS, H.   *Z. Kristallogr.* 1959, **112**, S.60.
22. LOOPSTRA, B. O.   Thesis, University of Amsterdam, September 1958.
23. HAMILTON, W. C. and IBERS, J.   *J. Phys. Soc. Japan* 1962, **17**, Suppl. B-II, 383.
24. GARRETT, B. S.   *Oak Ridge National Laboratory Report* No. 1745, 1954.
25. ROGERS, M. T. and HELMHOLZ, L.   *J. Amer. chem. Soc.* 1941, **63**, 278.
26. ATOJI, M. and RUNDLE, R. E.   *J. chem. Phys.* 1958, **29**, 1306.
27. This has recently been confirmed by nuclear magnetic resonance: VAN MEERSCHE, M., DEREPPE, J. M. and LOBO, P. W.   *Acta cryst.* 1962, **15**, 1310.
28. HAMILTON, W. C.   *Annual Review of Phys. Chemistry* 1962, **13**, 19.

CHAPTER 3

HYDROGEN ATOMS IN ORGANIC COMPOUNDS AND DETERMINATIONS OF MOLECULAR STRUCTURE

3.1. Introduction

In the previous chapter describing the location of hydrogen atoms in inorganic compounds, the interest has centred on the details of hydrogen bonds and the way in which they link together ions and groups of atoms in the crystal. When we turn to organic compounds we are inevitably more concerned with discrete molecules and with the concepts of molecular structure and molecular motion. We shall find that the information which neutron-diffraction studies can provide about the thermal motion of the hydrogen atoms is particularly valuable in obtaining a picture of the molecular motion as a whole, largely because it often happens that there are hydrogen atoms on the outer periphery of molecules and their linear motion when the whole molecule oscillates is therefore large. At the same time we shall still find much interest in the study of both inter- and intra-molecular hydrogen bonds. In many cases it will be clear that neutron studies have confirmed and put on a quantitative basis rather tentative suggestions which have been put forward as a result of earlier investigations using X-rays. In our discussion we shall consider some ring compounds first, then passing on to aliphatic compounds before returning at the end of the chapter to a discussion of centred hydrogen bonds in organic compounds, with both an aliphatic and aromatic example.

3.2. Some Aromatic and Related Ring Compounds

The first study reported of an aromatic compound, that of α-resorcinol m-$C_6H_4(OH)_2$ by Bacon and Curry,[1] provides a typical example. Fig. 3.1 gives a projection of the neutron-scattering density on the 001 plane of the orthorhombic structure and show very directly how inter-molecular hydrogen bonds link together the hydroxyl groups of adjoining molecules. This projection is a composite one. The carbon and

49

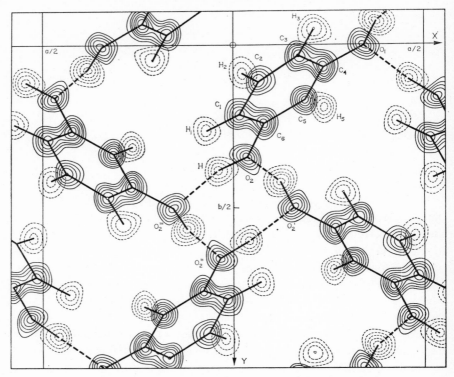

FIG. 3.1. A projection on the (001) plane of the neutron scattering density in α-resorcinol. The full lines represent positive contours from carbon and oxygen atoms, and the broken lines are negative contours from hydrogen atoms. The projection is a composite one: the carbon and oxygen atoms are taken from a complete synthesis but the hydrogen atom contours are the improved contours given by a "difference" synthesis. The hydroxyl groups from neighbouring molecules are linked to form infinite helices of hydrogen bonds through the crystal: in the two-dimensional projection these appear as the four-sided closed circuits such as $O_2\ O_2'\ O_2''\ O_2'''$. The molecules are inclined at 61° to the plane of the projection.

oxygen atoms are drawn as they appear from a direct synthesis of F_o but, in order to give as accurate details as possible, the hydrogen atom contours are the ones which appear in a "difference" projection obtained by synthesis of $(F_o - F_{CO})$. The hydrogen atoms H_1, H_3 are clearly resolved from their carbon atoms, but H_2, H_5 overlap C_2, C_5 respectively because of the inclination of the molecules to the plane of the projection. When the structure is considered in three dimensions the results substantiate Robertson's original picture of spirals of hydrogen bonds which run through the structure. The mean value of the C—H bond length was found to be 1·08 Å and although a standard deviation of no better than 0·04 Å was claimed it was clear that the results were entirely consistent with accepted values from infrared spectroscopy. We may note here that over the past ten years or so increasing accuracy has been obtained in the measurement of C—H bond lengths by X-ray methods also. There is some justification for the belief that when C—H bond lengths are measured with X-rays they are found to be shorter than the neutron and spectroscopic values, leading to the suggestion that the centre of the electron cloud for hydrogen is nearer to the carbon atom than is the proton. However, there are scarcely any examples of accurate measurements on the same compound by both techniques and the problem is still unresolved. Returning to our discussion of the structure of α-resorcinol, it is of interest to note that the results suggested some thermal motion of the molecule as a whole. The movement of carbon atom C_2 is larger than that of the atoms C_1, C_3, which in turn is greater than for the atoms C_4, C_5, C_6, and the same sequence of magnitudes is observed for the motion of the associated hydrogen atoms. It therefore appears that the carbon atoms C_4, C_6 are relatively firmly anchored by the hydrogen bonds and there is some motion of the molecule as a whole about the axis which joins these pivots.

A more marked example of molecular oscillation is provided by di-chloro di-phenyl sulphone $(p\text{-}ClC_6H_4)_2\ SO_2$ for which[2] the projection of the neutron scattering density is shown in Fig. 3.2. A least-squares analysis of the intensity data shows that there is considerable anisotropic motion of the atoms at the two ends of the molecule, furthest away from the SO_2 group. To a first approximation there is an oscillation, about carbon atom C_1, of the benzene ring and its chlorine atom. In contrast to most other cases, the X-ray[3] and neutron[2] studies of dichloro diphenyl sulphone were carried out concurrently. The neutron measurements were restricted to the 010 projection and only in one respect, namely the thermal motion of the sulphur atom which is a "light" atom for neutrons, was there any significant difference in the positional and thermal parameters determined independently by X-rays and neutrons. The average length of the four different carbon–hydrogen bonds is 1·05 Å.

Our two previous examples have both referred to aromatic molecules, one completely planar and the other with substantial planar sections. A contrasting case is provided by Andresen's study[4] of hexamethylene tetramine, $C_6H_4N_{12}$, the molecules of which are rather globular in shape. This substance is one of the very few organic compounds which crystallize in the cubic system and had previously been studied by several

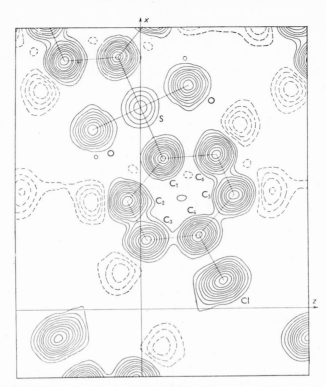

FIG. 3.2. A projection on the 010 plane of the neutron-scattering density
in 4,4′-dichloro di-phenyl sulphone. The molecule is symmetrical about the
sulphur atom and is not fully shown in the projection. Full lines are positive
contours: broken lines are the negative contours of the hydrogen atoms.
From its number of contours it will be noticed that sulphur is a light atom
for neutrons and has a scattering amplitude about equal to hydrogen, but
of opposite sign. (Bacon and Curry, *Acta cryst.* 1960, **13**, 10.)

investigators using X-rays. The neutron study substantiates in very
direct fashion what had been inferred with much less certainty from the
earlier work. The shape of the molecule, with its structural chemical
formula written alongside for comparison, is illustrated in Fig. 3.3,
together with the arrangement of the molecules in the unit cell of the
crystal structure. There are two molecules in the unit cell and the
neutron data demonstrate that these two molecules are identically
oriented in the unit cell, with the hydrogen atoms in the diagonal planes
of the unit cube. The evidence for this conclusion is given by projections
of neutron scattering density along the 1$\bar{1}$0) axis which are shown in
Fig. 3.4. In this projection, for which the line of sight is that marked in

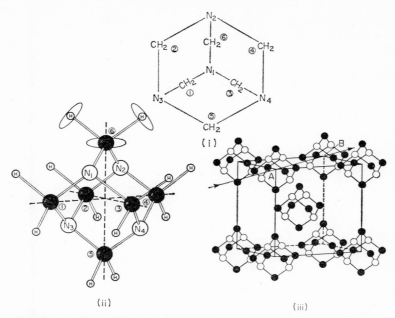

FIG. 3.3. A sketch (ii) of a molecule of hexamethylene-tetramine with its structural formula (i) written above. At (iii) is shown the arrangement of the molecules about the corners and body-centres of the unit-cell: for clarity the hydrogen atoms have been omitted in this view. The line-of-sight for the projections in Fig. 3.4 is along the direction N_1—N_2, i.e. along the face diagonal AB as indicated in (iii). In (ii) the shaded discs, which are only drawn for the top C and H atoms, indicate the thermal oscillation of the molecule about its centre. (After Robertson, J. M. *Organic Crystals and Molecules* Cornell University Press, 1953.)

our earlier Fig. 3.3, the bottom CH_2 group of a molecule at the corner of a unit cell just overlaps with the top CH_2 group of the molecule at the body-centre of the cell. The right-hand projection shows the contribution to the scattering density from the hydrogen atoms alone. In each case the line of sight is such that N_1, N_2 are superimposed, giving an intense peak, whereas, N_3, N_4 appear separately. In the same way $(CH_2)_1$, $(CH_2)_2$ and $(CH_2)_3$, $(CH_2)_4$ are superimposed in pairs. The neutron intensities are particularly significant in confirming the earlier suggestion, from the X-ray diffraction investigations, of an oscillation of the whole molecule about its centre. The effect of this motion is that each atom is smeared out into a substantial disc of scattering matter perpendicular to the radius vector from the centre of the molecule. Because of the large distance of the hydrogen atoms from the centre they show this effect most markedly and it is this type of oscillatory

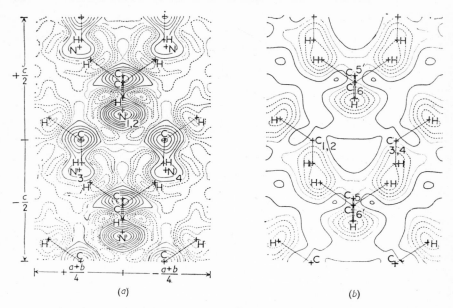

FIG. 3.4. Fourier projections on the $1\bar{1}0$ plane for the neutron scattering density in hexamethylene tetramine. (a) shows all the atoms in the structure, (b) shows only the hydrogen atoms. Contours are drawn at intervals of 100 units except for the positive peaks in (a) where the intervals are 200. The numbering of the nitrogen atoms and of the carbon atoms in the methylene groups are in accordance with diagrams (i), (ii), of Fig. 3.3.
(Andresen, *Acta cryst.* 1957, **10**, 109.)

motion which accounts for the marked ellipticity of some of the atoms in the projections. It was concluded that the radii of the discs, of which one or two are drawn in Fig. 3.3 (ii), were 0·35, 0·39 and 0·58 Å for the nitrogen, carbon and hydrogen atoms respectively. Superimposed on this oscillation of the whole molecule is an isotropic random motion of the individual atoms, amounting to a root-mean-square displacement of about 0·15 Å. When the neutron diffraction intensities were calculated for an atomic model with this composite type of thermal motion the "discrepancy factor" was reduced to the very low value of 3·2 per cent. Other conclusions from the study were that there is a C—H bond length of 1·13 Å in the methylene groups and that these C—H bonds form angles of 110° at the carbon atoms. The weak hydrogen bonds which the hydrogen atoms take part in, linking carbon and nitrogen atoms in adjacent molecules, are not strong enough to deform the tetrahedral angle within the methylene group nor to prevent the oscillation of the whole molecule as a single unit.

It will be noticed that practically all the investigations which we describe are only two dimensional and the pictures of the structures are limited to a view along some particular direction or, occasionally, along two or three directions. This rather limited scope of these studies arises because of the relatively long time which is needed for collecting the data, particularly in comparison with what can be done with the much more intense X-ray beams, but the limitation is often acceptable when the task of the neutron crystallographer is to clarify or complete some details of the partial picture revealed by X-rays. However, with the availability of higher-flux reactors, and the development of automatic methods of data collection many more full 3-dimensional analyses are now likely to appear. At the present moment we can only report one preliminary analysis in 3-dimensions. This has been made by Willis[5] for ferrocene, $C_{10}H_{10}Fe$, using a rather limited number of 230 *hkl* reflections.

Ferrocene is a "sandwich" molecule, consisting of an iron atom sandwiched between two cyclopentadienyl rings. The two problems in the investigation are, first, to see whether the hydrogen atoms lie in the plane of the rings and, secondly, to determine the relative orientation of the two five-membered carbon rings about the normal to their plane. It was concluded that the hydrogen atoms were co-planar with the carbon atoms within about 0·01 Å and that the C—H bond length was 1·09 ± 0·02 Å. The most interesting conclusion however was that at room temperature there is disorder in the orientation of the molecules. It is believed that the molecules have the "staggered" configuration illustrated in Fig. 3.5, but that both of the two orientations shown at (i), (ii) are present, roughly in the proportion of 2:1. This conclusion is

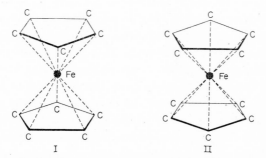

FIG. 3.5. The two possible staggered configurations of the ferrocene molecules which are believed to be present in the crystal in the proportions 2 : 1.

in quantitative agreement with the specific heat measurements of Edwards, Kington and Mason[6] who attributed an anomaly at 164°K to a change from a perfectly ordered to a partially ordered arrangement having the two orientations (i), (ii) distributed randomly throughout the structure.

3.3. Some Aliphatic Compounds

One of the earliest aliphatic compounds to be studied with neutrons is oxalic acid dihydrate $(COOH)_2 2H_2O$, which we could have discussed conveniently in the previous chapter with the inorganic hydrated salts. A projection of this substance on the 010 plane of the monoclinic unit cell, as obtained[7] by Garrett (1954), is illustrated in Fig. 3.6. It provides

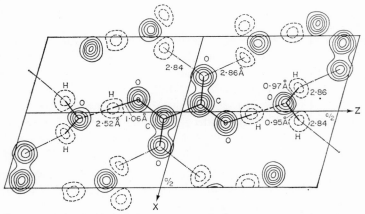

FIG. 3.6. A projection of the structure of oxalic acid dihydrate, showing the two types of hydrogen bond. The OH group in the carboxyl group is joined by a short hydrogen bond (2·52 Å) to the oxygen atom of a water molecule in the same hydrate complex. The carbonyl oxygen atom is linked by two weak bonds (measuring 2·84, 2·86 Å) to water molecules in neighbouring complexes. (Garrett, Ref. 7.)

a particularly good example of the presence of both "short" and "long" hydrogen bonds in the same structure. There is a short bond, of length 2·52 Å, which unites the hydroxyl group to the oxygen atom of a water molecule within the same molecular complex. Here the O—H distance is 1·06 Å, which is a relatively large distance and appropriate to the short O—O distance; moreover, the bond is almost linear. There is no evidence at all of either a centred bond or a disordered arrangement of hydrogens and the hydrogen atom is definitely associated with the hydroxyl grouping in the carboxyl group. The second type of bond, of which there are two examples is, however, much longer for they measure 2·84, 2·86 Å between the oxygen atom in the carbonyl group and oxygen atoms belonging to water molecules in neighbouring molecular complexes. Each carbonyl group is linked to two water molecules. These bonds are so weak that the protons in the water molecules which take part in them are practically as close to the water-oxygen atoms as they would be in a molecule of steam. In each case this type of bond is markedly non-linear and there are kinks of 13° and 24° respectively, at proton position for the two cases.

An example of a neutron study[8] of a fairly simple compound which had previously been intensively studied not only by X-ray diffraction[9] but also by other physical methods such as infra-red spectroscopy and proton magnetic resonance is provided by urea, $CO(NH_2)_2$. The crystal symmetry is tetragonal, with the space group $P\bar{4}2_1m$, and the arrangement and details of the molecular structure as revealed by neutron diffraction is shown in Fig. 3.7. Each unit cell contains two molecules, one of which

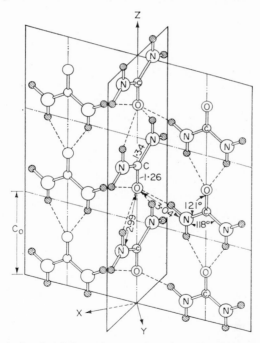

FIG. 3.7. A sketch of the structure of urea, indicating how the planar molecules lie in two sets of perpendicular 110 type planes. The hydrogen atoms are shaded. The dotted lines are drawn to complete the hydrogen bonds which link the nitrogen atoms to oxygen atoms in neighbouring molecules. (After Vaughan and Donohue, *Acta cryst.* 1952, **5**, 530.)

lies in each of the diagonal 110 planes: one molecule therefore lies in the main plane of the figure and the other is in the subsidiary perpendicular plane and is related to the first one by an inversion tetrad axis.

It is found that the hydrogen atoms (which are shaded in the figure) are co-planar with the rest of the molecule, and that they take part in hydrogen bonds which link each nitrogen atom to carbonyl oxygen atoms in two adjacent molecules. Both N—H distances are found to measure 0·99 Å. As always, these measured values are the *apparent* interatomic distances between the centroids of the distributions of atomic nuclei produced by the thermal motion, and the true equilibrium distances may be considerably greater, because of the large thermal motion in a direction perpendicular to the N—H bonds which is evident in the Fourier projection of Fig. 3.8. We have discussed this effect earlier, particularly in our account of AlO(OH) in Chapter 2, but in the present case it is much more difficult to calculate the correction than in our previous examples. This is because it is not possible either to

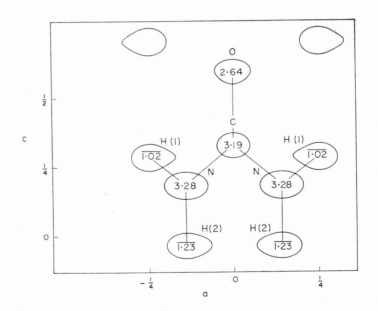

Fig. 3.8. An outline of the Fourier projection of a molecule of urea, as viewed along the b-axis at 45° to the plane of the molecule. The contours are drawn at positions where the scattering density has fallen to a half of the value at the atomic centres and their shapes thus indicate the very anisotropic thermal motion. The numbers at the atomic positions give the peak values of the scattering density. (Worsham *et al.*, *Acta cryst.* 1957, **10**, 319.)

regard the N, H motions as independent or to consider one of the motions as negligible. Indeed the general pattern of variation of the various temperature factors suggests that there is an oscillatory motion of the molecule as a whole and the movements of individual atoms appear to be strongly correlated. It is found that there is a definite correlation between the thermal displacement of an atom and its distance from the centre of gravity of the molecule.

Both of the hydrogen bonds, which are represented by the broken lines in Fig. 3.7, are very weak, with overall N—O separations of 2·99 and 3·03 Å respectively, and it is therefore not surprising, in view of our observations from other substances, to find that these bonds are considerably bent. The angles at the positions of the hydrogen atoms are 152° and 167° in the two cases. The three inter-bond angles at the nitrogen atom are very nearly equal, measuring 118°, 120° and 122° respectively.

Recently, some further X-ray measurements of the $h0l$ and $hk0$ reflections of urea have been made[10] by Sklar, Senko and Post, both at room temperature and at −140°C. Their conclusions show no statistically significant differences in position parameters, compared with previous measurements, but there are some apparently significant differences among the anisotropic thermal parameters, compared with the neutron data. It is not at all clear whether these differences are due to experimental or interpretative errors, such as wrong assumptions about X-ray scattering curves, or whether they indicate an actual distinction between the electronic and nuclear motions. Accurate data on many substances are essential before any general conclusions on this topic can be safely drawn.

Another compound which contains O—H——N bonds is dimethyl glyoxime

$$CH_3—C{=}N—OH$$
$$\,\,\,\,\,\,\,\,\,\,\,\,\,|$$
$$CH_3—C{=}N—OH$$

Hamilton[11] has refined the crystal structure and has shown that adjacent molecules are linked by normal O—H——N hydrogen bonds. There is no evidence of a "zwitterion" type of structure which has sometimes been proposed for oximes. The hydrogen bond network, which is practically planar, has the dimensions shown in Fig. 3.9, which makes clear the large departure of the hydrogen bond from linearity. This supports the general conclusion that spatial considerations in the local environment and the tendency of covalent bonds

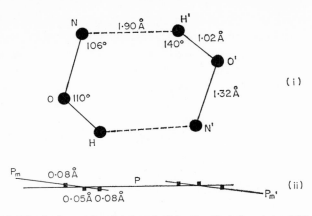

FIG. 3.9. The hydrogen-bond network (i) in dimethyl glyoxime which links together N—OH groupings in neighbouring molecules. In (ii) this almost-planar network is viewed end-on. The line P indicates the "best plane" through the 6 atoms and P_m, P_m' are the sections of the two molecular planes, which make angles of 7° with the plane of P (Hamilton, *Acta cryst.* 1961, **14**, 95.)

to remain undistorted readily outweigh any inherent tendency of the hydrogen bond to be linear.

Another interesting example is the completion of the structure[12] of pentaerythritol $C(CH_2OH)_4$ which has been intensively studied previously with X-rays. The shape of the molecule, without specifying the positions of the hydrogen atoms, is clear from Fig. 3.10. The central carbon atom is surrounded tetrahedrally by the four CH_2OH groups and neighbouring molecules are then linked by hydrogen bonds of length 2·7 Å. The final picture of the structure which emerges from Hvoslef's neutron diffraction investigation[12] is illustrated in Fig. 3.11 which is a projection along the c-axis of the tetragonal structure. Two layers of molecules overlap in the projection and as a consequence of this, the deduction of the hydrogen atom positions from an analysis of the neutron intensities of the $hk0$ and $0kl$ reflections is made difficult by the overlapping of the hydrogen atoms in the methylene and hydroxyl groups. In order to assist the interpretation of the data, comparisons were made of the neutron intensities for the two compounds $C(CH_2OH)_4$ and $C(CH_2OD)_4$: in the latter compound deuterium has replaced only the hydroxy hydrogen atoms of the ordinary material. These atoms are the ones which are shaded in Fig. 3.11. If $F_o{}^H$ and $F_o{}^D$ are the structure amplitude factors for the two compounds, then a synthesis of $(F_o{}^H F{-}_o{}^D)$ will display only the hydroxy type of hydrogen atoms.

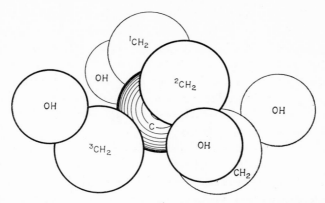

FIG. 3.10. The shape of a molecule of pentaerythritol, C(CH₂OH)₄, without showing the hydrogen atoms. The central carbon atom is surrounded tetrahedrally by four CH₂OH groups. (Shiono, Cruickshank and Cox, *Acta cryst.* 1958, **11**, 389.)

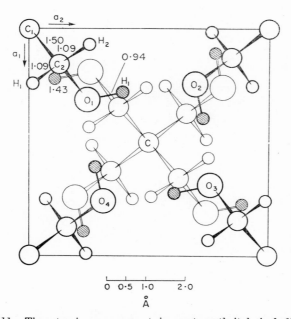

FIG. 3.11. The atomic arrangement in pentaerythritol, including the hydrogen atoms, as seen in projection on the 001 plane. The heavy lines indicate molecules which lie with their centre carbon atoms in the plane of the projection, at the corners of the unit cell: the weaker lines show the molecule at the body-centre of the cell at $z = \frac{1}{2}$. The hydroxy hydrogen atoms (which can be replaced by deuterium) are shown shaded. (Hvoslef, *Acta cryst.* 1958, **11**, 383.)

The projection can be normalized to the amplitude of the deuterium atoms by multiplying by the factor $b_D/(b_D - b_H)$, where b_D, b_H are the scattering amplitudes of deuterium and hydrogen respectively. The resulting projection will therefore show simply the deuterium atoms in $C(CH_2OD)_4$. The main criticism that could be applied to this procedure is that it assumes that the thermal parameters of hydrogen and deuterium are the same. However, using the parameters obtained in this way the discrepancy factor for the neutron data from $C(CH_2OH)_4$ was reduced to 6·1 per cent. Figure 3.12 gives the resulting projection of the deuterium atoms in $C(CH_2OD)_4$, and this establishes plainly that these atoms are in ordered positions, leading to the overall picture of the ordinary hydrogenated material which we have already shown in Fig. 3.11, with the hydroxy atom H_1 much closer to O_1 than to O_2. The bond length $O_1 - H_1$ is given as $0.94 \pm .03$ Å but this value may suffer from some shortening because of the anisotropic motion of the hydrogen atoms, which is very evident in Fig. 3.12.

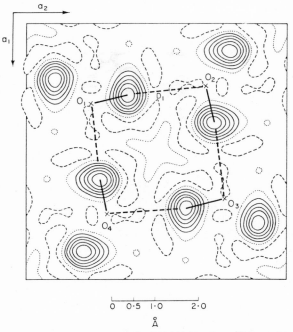

FIG. 3.12. A projection on the 001 plane of the "hydroxy" deuterium atoms only in the compound $C(CH_2OD)_4$. This projection proves that these hydroxy atoms are in the ordered positions which are shown shaded in Fig. 3.11, thus forming unsymmetrical hydrogen bonds to the neighbouring molecules. (Hvoslef, *Acta cryst.* 1958, **11**, 383.)

The most ambitious attempt at a full crystal-structure analysis with neutrons has been the investigation of Rochelle salt, $KNa(CHOH.COO)_2.4H_2O$ by Frazer and Pepinsky.[13] Although a detailed analysis has not been possible some interesting information about the structure of this ferro-electric crystal has been obtained. The magnitude of the problem is indicated by the fact that it is necessary to determine 504 parameters in order to achieve a 3-dimensional refinement, and there are 280 parameters for a 2-dimensional projection. As a result of the pseudosymmetry of the structure there are strong interactions between many of the parameters which add greatly to the problems of refinement. It is the slight deviations from non-polar symmetry which give rise to the spontaneous polarization, and it is the high-angle reflections in the diffraction pattern which are most sensitive to the small displacements which are involved. Neutrons have a marked advantage here because they are free from the substantial uncertainties in atomic scattering factor at high angles which occur for X-rays. Moreover, it appears that there is a significant amount of micro-structural damage when ferro-electrics are irradiated by X-rays, thus casting some doubt on the detailed structure as revealed by X-ray diffraction. It was found possible in the neutron study to confirm most of the hydrogen bond network originally proposed by Beevers and Hughes,[14] but the suggestion that the ferro-electricity was associated with ordering of the hydrogen atoms, somewhat as in the case of KH_2PO_4, was disproved. However, there appeared to be a noteworthy change of orientation of the hydroxyl group in the tartrate molecule, involving a substantial movement of the hydrogen atom, which may be significant in accounting for the properties of the ferro-electric phase.

3.4. Centred Hydrogen Bonds in Organic Structures

In our discussion of the inorganic compounds KHF_2 and KH_2PO_4 we mentioned the difficulty of trying to distinguish between true centring and statistical centring in short hydrogen bonds. Similar interesting examples are found among organic compounds and several of them have been examined with neutrons. In each case it is an intra-molecular hydrogen bond which is involved and the crystallographic location is such as to require either true or statistical centring of the hydrogen atom. A simple example in a small molecule exists in potassium hydrogen maleate $KH(CH.COO)_2$ which was studied[15] by Peterson and Levy. Their difference projection, showing only the hydrogen atoms, is illustrated in Fig. 3.13. As is usual in these cases, the scattering density is elongated along the O—O bond and the contours can be interpreted either in terms of a centred model, with anisotropic thermal motion, or by a disordered model with two half-hydrogens placed, in this example, at 1·05 Å from O_2 and O_2' respectively. A detailed analysis of the thermal motion leads to the surprising result that the movement of the hydrogen atom H_1 in the direction of the y-axis, which is at right-angles

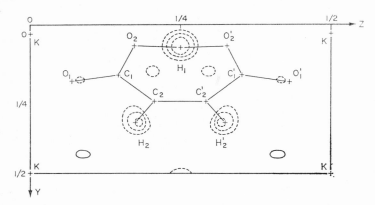

Fig. 3.13. A projection of the neutron scattering density of the hydrogen atoms in potassium hydrogen maleate KH (CH.COO)$_2$, on the 100 plane. Broken lines are negative contours. The positions of the other atoms in the structure are marked by crosses. (Peterson and Levy, *J. chem. Phys.* 1958, **29**, 948.)

to the O—O bond, is less than the movement of the oxygen atoms O_2, O_2'. This suggests a mode of motion within the molecule such that the oxygen atoms are displaced without any appreciable displacement of the hydrogen atom H_1.

Extensive studies of an aromatic acid salt, potassium hydrogen bisphenylacetate KH(C$_6$H$_5$CH$_2$COO)$_2$, have been made by Bacon and Curry, both at room temperature[16] and at 120°K,[17] where the thermal motion is reduced, and these are strongly in favour of a truly centred hydrogen bond. An extended view of the structure of this compound, which has monoclinic symmetry but with an angle β very close to 90°, is shown in Fig. 3.14. The acidic hydrogen atom concerned is the one at the centre of the molecule, which is linked on either side to an oxygen atom, with an O—O separation of 2·54 Å. The results of the neutron study, so far as the hydrogen atoms are concerned, are expressed in the projections in Fig. 3.15 which are drawn for the two temperatures of measurement. At room temperature, diagram (i), we again have the familiar slightly elliptical contours for the hydrogen atom H_0, slightly extended along the O—O bond. In diagram (ii) for the lower temperature, where the thermal motion is reduced, this type of anisotropy is not observed and, in fact, the thermal displacement is greater at right angles to the bond than it is in the O—O direction. The conclusion from a least-squares analysis of the data is that the direction of minimum thermal motion is along the O—O bond, and the magnitude of it is

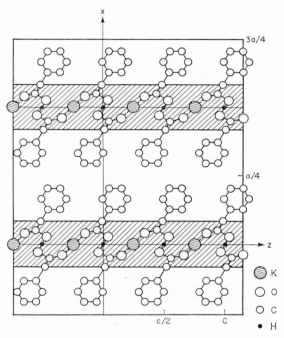

Fig. 3.14. An extended view of the structure of potassium hydrogen bis-phenylacetate, as seen along the y-axis. The tightly-bound shaded layers, held together by the potassium and hydrogen atoms, are to be contrasted with the loose open arrangement at the ends of the molecules at $x = a/4$ and $3a/4$. (Bacon and Curry, *Acta cryst.* 1960, **13**, 717.)

equal to only about 70 per cent of that in the perpendicular direction. In assessing the significance of this conclusion a critical view of the accuracy which can be achieved in the measurements is of great importance: the authors conclude that the differences in the vibration amplitudes are significant and that a two-position statistical model is ruled out in favour of a single centred hydrogen atom. This conclusion is strongly supported by the infra-red investigations[18] of Hadzi, Blinc and Novak who have studied the spectra of many acid salts, including those of potassium hydrogen maleate and potassium hydrogen bisphenyl-acetate. These spectra have characteristic features which are considered to be compatible only with a potential function which has a single symmetrical minimum.

Before leaving these compounds we would draw attention to the way in which the two projections in Fig. 3.15 indicate the value of a

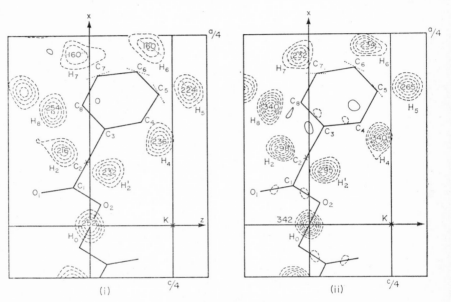

FIG. 3.15. The neutron scattering density due to hydrogen atoms only in potassium hydrogen bis-phenylacetate, projected on the 010 plane for (i) room temperature and (ii) 120°K. Practically all the contours are negative, because of the negative scattering amplitude of hydrogen. The peak heights of the atoms are indicated in arbitrary units. The diffuseness of the outer hydrogens, particularly in (i), is due to the molecular oscillation. In (ii) the contours of the hydrogen atom H_O at the origin support the conclusion that its thermal motion along the O—O bond direction is less than in the perpendicular direction, leading to the belief that this hydrogen bond is centred. (Bacon and Curry, *Acta cryst.* 1960, **13**, 717.)

knowledge of the detailed shapes of the hydrogen atom contours in any assessment of molecular motion. The enhanced motion of the hydrogen atoms at room temperature is very noticeable for the outer atoms H_6 and H_7 and it is also clear that their motion is very anisotropic. In the directions of maximum movement their Debye B factors are 16·5 and 14·5 Å² respectively. These B factors are equal to $80\overline{u^2}$ where $\overline{u^2}$ is the mean-square amplitude of the motion. A detailed analysis of the thermal parameters of the hydrogen and other atoms leads to the conclusion that the ends of the molecules "wag" about the carbon atoms C_3 and that the root-mean-square amplitude of this oscillation is about 5° of angle at room temperature and 4° at 120°K. Such a motion is consistent with the molecular environment which we illustrated in Fig. 3.14, for the structure is quite open and loose at the ends of the molecules in contrast with the strong linkages within the central, shaded layers where there is an octahedral grouping of oxygen atoms around the potassium ion and a short, strong hydrogen bond across the centre of symmetry.

REFERENCES

1. BACON, G. E. and CURRY, N. A.   *Proc. roy. Soc.* A. 1956, **235**, 552.
2. BACON, G. E. and CURRY, N. A.   *Acta cryst.* 1960, **13**, 10.
3. SIME, J. G. and ABRAHAMS, S. C.   *Acta cryst.* 1960, **13**, 1.
4. ANDRESEN, A. F.   *Acta cryst.* 1957, **10**, 109.
5. WILLIS, B. T. M.   *Acta cryst.* 1960, **13**, 1088.
6. EDWARDS, J. W., KINGTON, G. L. and MASON, R.   *Trans. Faraday Soc.* 1960, **56**, 660.
7. GARRETT, B. S.   *Oak Ridge National Laboratory Report* No. 1745, 1954.
8. WORSHAM, J. E., LEVY, H. A. and PETERSON, S. W.   *Acta cryst.* 1957, **10**, 319.
9. VAUGHAN, P. and DONOHUE, J.   *Acta cryst.* 1952, **5**, 530.
10. SKLAR, N., SENKO, M. E. and POST, B.   *Acta cryst.* 1961, **14**, 716.
11. HAMILTON, W. C.   *Acta cryst.* 1961, **14**, 95.
12. HVOSLEF, J.   *Acta cryst.* 1958, **11**, 383.
13. FRAZER, B. C.   *Journ. Phys. Soc. Japan*, 1962, **17**, Suppl. B-II, 376.
14. BEEVERS, C. A. and HUGHES, W.   *Proc. roy. Soc.* A. 1941, **177**, 251.
15. PETERSON, S. W. and LEVY, H. A.   *J. chem. Phys.* 1958, **29**, 948.
16. BACON, G. E. and CURRY, N. A.   *Acta cryst.* 1957, **10**, 524.
17. BACON, G. E. and CURRY, N. A.   *Acta cryst.* 1960, **13**, 717.
18. BLINC, R. and HADZI, D.   *Spectrochimica Acta*, 1960, **16**, 853.

CHAPTER 4

HEAVY ELEMENT COMPOUNDS OF CARBON, NITROGEN AND OXYGEN

ALTHOUGH the location of hydrogen atoms in both inorganic and organic compounds has proved one of the most attractive applications for neutron diffraction, thus overcoming the limitations set on X-ray methods by the circumstance that the hydrogen atom contains only one electron, the contribution to heavy element chemistry by locating atoms such as carbon, nitrogen and oxygen must not be overlooked. Elements such as the rare earths and uranium have X-ray scattering amplitudes which are ten or twenty times greater than those of carbon, nitrogen and oxygen and, as a result, these latter elements make very little contribution to the X-ray diffraction patterns of their compounds. There is therefore very little direct evidence of the positions of these lighter atoms in heavy element compounds and they have usually been deduced indirectly from considerations of atomic size and packing. Quite a number of such compounds have now been studied with neutrons, mainly using only polycrystalline samples. Fortunately powder methods of analysis have usually proved adequate to distinguish between alternative structural possibilities in these relatively simple structures.

4.1. Oxides and Related Compounds

Among the oxides of heavy elements which have been examined are La_2O_3, Sc_2O_3, U_3O_8 and UO_2, PbO and AgO.

A typical example of the way in which a simple distinction can be made between two possible atomic arrangements is provided by Koehler and Wollan's study[1] of La_2O_3 and the related oxides Pr_2O_3 and Nd_2O_3. In the past, two possible arrangements illustrated in Fig. 4.1 had been suggested by Zachariasen[2] and Pauling[3] respectively, for the locations of the oxygen atoms in the hexagonal unit cells. The former model could be eliminated by a first inspection of the neutron diffraction pattern since it would lead to quite intense (001) and (111) reflections, whereas these reflections were found to be immeasurably small. The significance of the measurement of the 001 reflection can be appreciated quite readily from Fig. 4.1. For this reflection there is no contribution from the metal atoms in either model since they lie in planes separated by $c/2$ and successive planes give mutual cancellation. In model (ii) the oxygen atoms would clearly give mutual reinforcement and an intense reflection for 001 whereas from model (i) only a very small resultant contribution is expected. This study provides a very good example of how a structural controversy of long standing can some-times be solved by a very simple neutron measurement.

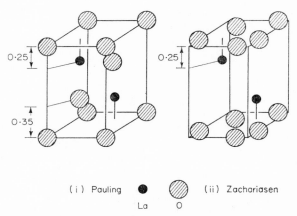

(i) Pauling   ● ⊘ (ii) Zachariasen

La   O

FIG. 4.1. The suggestions made for the structure of the rare-earth sesqui-oxides by Pauling (i) and Zachariasen (ii).

Scandium oxide, Sc_2O_3, has been studied[4] by Milligan *et al.* and con-firmed to have the cubic thallic oxide structure, with space group $Ia3$. There are four positional parameters to be determined for this structure (one for the metal atoms and three to define the oxygen positions) and the values deduced from the neutron data were the same as those given by an X-ray study[5] of the related mineral bixbyite $(Fe, Mn)_2O_3$. The same workers have also confirmed that scandium orthovanadate $ScVO_4$ has the expected zircon structure. There is an interesting point of detail which appears here when the X-ray and neutron diffraction intensities are compared. With X-rays many reflections with the l index odd were absent because the X-ray scattering amplitudes of V^{5+} and Sc^{3+} are equal, and the contributions from the two ions are out of phase for these reflections, leaving only the scattering by the atoms of oxygen, which is very small. With neutrons this cancellation does not happen for not only is the vanadium scattering amplitude very small, and of opposite sign, compared with scandium but also the oxygen contribution is very substantial.

The uranium oxides have been studied by several workers and there continues to be great interest in this subject because of the important role of these oxides in ceramic nuclear fuels. Andresen[6] has concluded from neutron powder diffraction patterns that the structure assumed for U_3O_8 on the basis of X-ray data is not correct. The original and subsequently suggested structures are compared in Fig. 4.2. In diagram (i) in this figure, which was derived by Zachariasen on the basis of

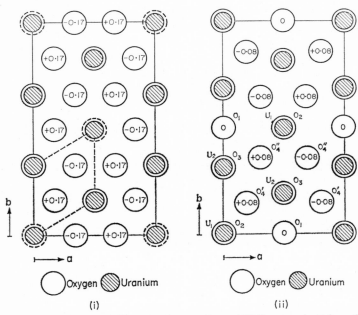

FIG. 4.2. Diagrams to illustrate the structure of U_3O_8 as projected on the 001 plane. Diagram (i) is the structure first proposed by Zachariasen, based on the close relation with the α-UO_3 structure: oxygen atoms corresponding to the dotted rings are removed. (ii) is the structure suggested by Andresen from the neutron diffraction study. (Andresen, *Acta cryst.* 1958, **11**, 612.)

the close similarity between U_3O_8 and the α-UO_3 structure, the dotted oxygen atoms in the position $(00\frac{1}{2})$ and $(\frac{1}{2}\frac{1}{2}\frac{1}{2})$ have to be removed, thus giving a structure which has the correct ratio of oxygen to uranium atoms to fit the composition U_3O_8. Such a model would give a strong (131) neutron reflection but although there is considerable overlapping of reflections in the powder diagram it is evident that there is very little scattering at the angular position of this particular reflection. In the new structure which is shown at (ii) in Fig. 4.2 the reduced oxygen content is achieved by amalgamating pairs of oxygen atoms into single atoms at $(\frac{1}{2}00)$ and $(0\frac{1}{2}0)$ and, at the same time, providing more room at these positions by slight displacements of the neighbouring uranium atoms. The resulting structure favours the conclusion that each molecule contains $2U^{5+}$ ions and one U^{6+}, in agreement with deductions from magnetic measurements, whereas the earlier model predicted one U^{4+} ion and two U^{6+} ions.

The structure of UO_2 and the way in which this compound can take up extra oxygen to form non-stoichiometric compounds such as $UO_{2.1}$ has been studied[7] by Willis. This work has been done with single-crystals and confirms that UO_2 itself has a simple fluorite type of structure with the metal atoms at the corners and face-centres of the unit cell and eight oxygen atoms at the points $\frac{1}{4}\frac{1}{4}\frac{1}{4}$ and the other seven related positions. For the composition $UO_{2.1}$ both X-ray diffraction and density measurements suggest that the number and positions of the uranium atoms remains unchanged and that the departure from stoichiometry is due to an excess of oxygen atoms. The neutron intensities are consistent with the belief that these extra oxygen atoms are distributed among the holes which are present in the structure at $\frac{1}{2}\frac{1}{2}\frac{1}{2}$, $\frac{1}{2}00$, $0\frac{1}{2}0$ and $00\frac{1}{2}$. At the same time, in order to minimize the strain around the interstitial oxygen atoms, there is a displacement of the nearby "ordinary" oxygen atoms from their regular positions such as $\frac{1}{4}\frac{1}{4}\frac{1}{4}$ to uuu where u is equal to about 0.20. Figure 4.3 indicates the displacements of the oxygen atoms in the neighbourhood of one of the "extra" oxygen atoms. For the initial incorporation of oxygen the extra atoms are probably distributed at random in the UO_2 structure but with further increase of oxygen the U_4O_9 phase appears: this is an ordered structure with a multiple unit cell in comparison with the simple cell of UO_2.

Silver oxide, AgO, is an example of a compound which neutrons have shown[8] to have a structure of lower symmetry than was believed from X-ray diffraction results. It has a monoclinic unit cell and was believed to belong to space group $C2/c$ but a neutron diffraction study, which was able to locate the oxygen atoms much more accurately, showed the space group to be only $P2_1/c$. The greater accuracy is achieved because the neutron scattering length for oxygen, 0.58×10^{-12} cm, is almost as large as that for silver, 0.61×10^{-12} cm. The modified structure reveals that there are two types of silver atoms, which are different crystallographically, and the measured bond lengths and co-ordination are consistent with the presence of Ag^+ and Ag^{+++} ions. They are not consistent with the presence of the Ag^{2+} ion, which has an unpaired electron and would be paramagnetic. The absence of any magnetic scattering, which was sought for down to liquid-helium temperature, supports the conclusion that AgO is diamagnetic.

The yellow orthorhombic form of lead monoxide, PbO, has been studied, from powder patterns, both by Kay[9] and by Leciejewicz.[10] Its structure is found to be a distortion of the tetragonal red form in which layers of oxygen atoms are sandwiched between layers of lead. In the orthorhombic form the oxygen layers are puckered and the pyramidal PbO$_4$ groups are much distorted.

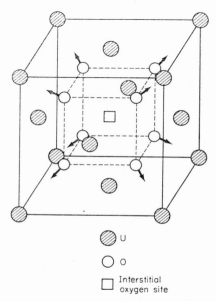

U

O

Interstitial
oxygen site

Fig. 4.3. The unit cell of uranium dioxide UO$_2$. There are holes in the structure at $\frac{1}{2}\frac{1}{2}\frac{1}{2}$ (marked by a square) and at $\frac{1}{2}00$, $0\frac{1}{2}0$ and $00\frac{1}{2}$. At the composition UO$_{2.1}$ it is believed that interstitial oxygen atoms are incorporated in some of the holes and the "ordinary" oxygen atoms are displaced outwards slightly to accommodate them as indicated by the arrows. (Willis, Ref. 7.)

The titanates BaTiO$_3$ and PbTiO$_3$ are of particular interest because of their ferro-electric properties and the related compounds such as PbZrO$_3$, NaNbO$_3$ and PbHfO$_3$ are antiferro-electric. Above a certain temperature these compounds all have a cubic perovskite type of structure which is illustrated in Fig. 4.4 but at room temperature there are slight displacements of the atoms from the ideal positions, resulting in either tetragonal or orthorhombic symmetry. The unusual electric properties are associated with these atomic shifts and their measurement is important in seeking to get a better understanding of the nature of the ferro-electricity. The use of neutron diffraction to supplement X-ray data has been particularly useful in determining the precise positions of the oxygen atoms, which are difficult to locate very accurately with X-rays in the presence of heavy atoms such as barium and lead. With neutrons the situation is much more favourable since oxygen, for which b is $0\cdot58 \times 10^{-12}$ cm, has a slightly larger scattering amplitude than barium ($b = 0\cdot53 \times 10^{-12}$ cm) and it is not grossly inferior to that of lead, for which b is $0\cdot96 \times 10^{-12}$ cm. Details of the

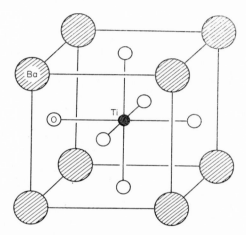

Fig. 4.4. The perovskite structure of the titanates and zirconates, as typified by $BaTiO_3$. Above 120°C it has the ideal cubic structure shown but at lower temperatures it becomes tetragonal and the atoms are slightly displaced from the ideal positions.

atomic positions can be found in the literature for $BaTiO_3$, of which single-crystals have been studied by Frazer, Danner and Pepinsky,[11] and for $PbTiO_3$[12] and $PbZrO_3$[13] which have been examined in powder form by Pepinsky and his co-workers.

4.2. Carbides

Many metal carbides of the form MC_2 and M_2C_3 have been described in a series of papers[14, 15, 16, 34] by Atoji and his co-workers. Previous X-ray studies had failed to determine the carbon atom positions with much accuracy because of the comparatively small scattering amplitude of carbon for X-rays. Typical examples are CaC_2, LaC_2 and UC_2 and these compounds have the body centred tetragonal structure indicated in Fig. 4.5. The metal atom positions are 000 and $\frac{1}{2}\frac{1}{2}\frac{1}{2}$, with the carbons at $(000, \frac{1}{2}\frac{1}{2}\frac{1}{2}) \pm 00z$, so that the C_2 dumb-bells lie between pairs of metal atoms. The aim of the analysis is to determine the z-parameter for the carbon atoms, which is related to the C—C distance in the C_2 groups by $d_{C-C} = 2c(\frac{1}{2} - z)$ where c is the height of the unit cell. The procedure followed was to calculate the neutron intensities for a series of values of z and then compare them with the values observed experimentally. Only powdered samples were available and very few of the reflections were completely resolved. The comparison was made therefore by making summations over groups of lines and then determining discrepancy

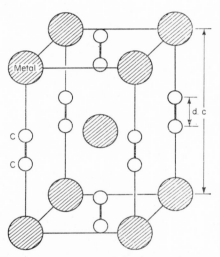

Fig. 4.5. The CaC$_2$-type structure of the heavy-element carbides. The C—C distance, d, in the C_2 groups is equal to $2c(\frac{1}{2} - z)$, where z is the parameter which defines the distance of the carbon atoms from the corners and body-centres of the unit cell.

factors such as $R_1 = \sum |I_{obs} - I_{calc}| / \sum I_{obs}$ which are a measure of the extent of disagreement between the actual structure and the postulated model. The parameter z was then chosen to give a minimum value for the discrepancy factor. Figure 4.6 illustrates the deduction of the values of z for CaC$_2$ and UC$_2$. In the former case the C—C distance turns out to be 1·20 Å which is the same as is found for the triple bond in acetylene, but quite different from 1·4 Å which was originally deduced by X-rays. The occurrence of a triple bond distance in CaC$_2$ is very satisfactory since it is an ionic crystal and the electronic state of an isolated

$(C_2)^{2-}$ group should be the same as that of the molecule N_2, which contains the same number of electrons. In uranium carbide, which is metallic and has an electronic conductivity comparable with that of uranium metal, the C—C distance is 1·34 Å which corresponds to a double bond, C=C. Lanthanum carbide is an intermediate case with C—C equal to 1·28 Å. These interatomic distances are discussed by Atoji and others[15, 34] in relation to the electronic configuration of the C_2 groups. For example, with the lanthanum ion being present as La^{3+} in LaC_2 we can write this compound as $La^{3+} C_2^{2-}$, together with an extra electron in a conduction band which will account for the observed conductivity, which is comparable with that of metallic lanthanum. These studies have been extended further by Atoji[16] to include also the dicarbides YC_2, CeC_2, TbC_2, YbC_2 and LuC_2. In each case the intensity data were examined by least-squares analysis. It is found that there is very close agreement between the C—C values in all the rare-earth

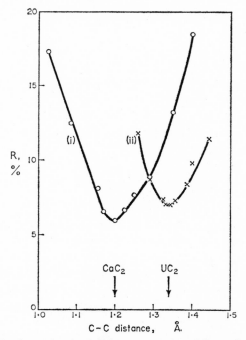

Fig. 4.6. The determination of the z parameter of the carbon atoms for (i) CaC_2 and (ii) UC_2. For various values of the C—C distance the neutron diffraction intensities I_{calc} are computed. The discrepancy factor $R_1 = \Sigma|I_{obs} - I_{calc}|/\Sigma I_{obs}$ is then calculated and plotted against the C—C distance. Best agreement is obtained for C—C = 1·20 Å for CaC_2 and 1·34 Å for UC_2. (From Atoji and Medrud, *J. chem. Phys.* 1959, **31**, 332.)

dicarbides and there are no significant differences from the weighted-average value of $1 \cdot 278 \pm 0 \cdot 002$ Å. Summarizing we may say that CaC_2, LaC_2 (for example) and UC_2 behave as $M^{2+}C_2$, $M^{3+}C_2$ and $M^{4+}C_2$ and that the C—C distance increases as the metallic valency increases.

The electronic states of the atoms in these dicarbides have been examined further by Atoji[16] by means of measurements of their paramagnetic scattering. In our general discussion of magnetic scattering in Chapter 1 we defined the magnetic scattering amplitude p which we saw was proportional to the spin quantum number S if the orbital moment is quenched, and to the quantum number J in the general case represented by the rare-earth ions. In the case of ferromagnetic or antiferromagnetic solids there will be co-operative interference between the scattered contributions from neighbouring atoms but for paramagnetic solids, where the magnetic moments point randomly, each atom scatters independently and increases the background scattering. The amount of this scattering per unit solid angle or the "differential cross-section" for paramagnetic scattering, is roughly equal to p^2. However, in order to assess the scattering exactly we must take account of the fact that the direction in which the magnetic moment of an atom points may be different after the atom has scattered a neutron compared with its initial direction—though this is not the case for *aligned* moments in ferromagnetic or antiferromagnetic solids. As a result of this extra randomness, the factor S^2 in the expression for p^2 which we get from equation (1.5.1) has to be replaced by $S(S + 1)$ and the scattering per unit solid angle becomes[17]

$$\frac{\mathrm{d}\sigma}{\mathrm{d}\omega} = \frac{2}{3} \left(\frac{e^2 \gamma}{mc^2} \right)^2 S(S + 1) f^2 \qquad (4.2.1)$$

The factor $\frac{2}{3}$ takes into account the randomness in the arrangement of the magnetic moments relative to the scattering vector. This randomness is important because, as we stated in Chapter 1, the full value of the magnetic scattering amplitude is only achieved if the moment direction is perpendicular to the scattering vector. In the more general case, however, where the orbital angular momentum is not quenched we have to replace eqn. (1) by[17]

$$\frac{\mathrm{d}\sigma}{\mathrm{d}\omega} = \frac{2}{3} \left(\frac{e^2 \gamma}{mc^2} \right)^2 g^2 J(J + 1) f^2 \qquad (4.2.2)$$

where g is the Landé splitting factor.

To allow for the different form factors associated with the orbital and spin moment this expression is usually written in the form due to Trammell[18] as

$$\left(\frac{d\sigma}{d\omega}\right)_k = \frac{2}{3}\left(\frac{e^2\gamma}{2mc^2}\right)^2 [L_J f_L(k) + 2S_J f_S(k)]^2 \qquad (4.2.3)$$

where $L_J \equiv \mathbf{L}\cdot\mathbf{J}/|\mathbf{J}|$ and $S_J = \mathbf{S}\cdot\mathbf{J}/|\mathbf{J}|$ and the orbital and spin form factors $f_L(k), f_S(k)$ can be calculated at any value of $k \equiv (\sin\theta)/\lambda$ from screened hydrogenic wave functions for the atoms. The quantities L_J, S_J are the resolved components of the orbital and spin vectors in the direction of the resultant angular momentum vector $\mathbf{J}$. Their numerical values are equal to $\{J(J+1)\pm[L(L+1)-S(S+1)]\}/2[J(J+1)]^{\frac{1}{2}}$ respectively. The screening constant for the $4f$ electrons in the rare earths is an adjustable parameter in the calculation and can be determined from the experimental data. The procedure which is used in practice can be followed for a typical example such as cerium carbide CeC_2 discussed by Atoji.[16] Curve (i) in Fig. 4.7 shows the observed background scattering for this compound as a function of $(\sin\theta)/\lambda$. From this we have to subtract the thermal diffuse scattering, curve (ii),

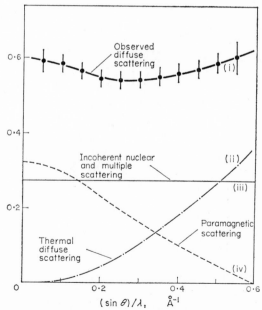

FIG. 4.7. The deduction of the curve (iv) for paramagnetic scattering by CeC_2 as a function of $(\sin\theta)/\lambda$. (Atoji, *J. chem. Phys.* 1961, **35**, 1950.)

which can be calculated in terms of the Debye theory, and also the incoherent scattering from various sources, which is assumed to be isotropic and can be deduced from the fact that at high values of θ it must account for the whole of the difference between curves (i) and (ii). The value of this scattering is therefore represented by the constant level (iii) and this in turn leads to the conclusion, by subtraction of curves (ii) and (iii) from curve (i), that the paramagnetic scattering is given by curve (iv). This resulting curve is shown again in Fig. 4.8, with an indication of the experimental inaccuracies of the individual points, together with theoretical curves which have been calculated for various values of the screening constant s. The figure indicates that the value of $Z - s$ is about 19 so that the screening constant for the $4f$ electrons in cerium (which has atomic number 58) is 39. The intercept of the curve at $\theta = 0°$ can be compared with the value calculated from eqn. (2), when f is put equal to unity, for any assumed ionic state. If the

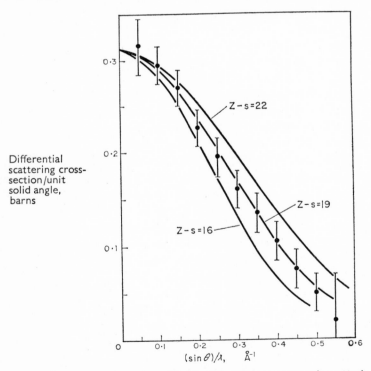

Fig. 4.8. The variation with $(\sin \theta)/\lambda$ of the paramagnetic scattering cross-section for Ce in CeC_2. The solid curves are calculated for various screening constants s and suggest that $Z - s = 19$. (Atoji, *J. chem. Phys.* 1961, **35**, 1950.)

cerium ion is in the Ce^{3+} state the values of S, L and J for the $4f$ electrons will be $\frac{1}{2}$, 3 and 5/2 respectively, corresponding to the state $^2F_{5/2}$ and from eqn. (2) it is then calculated that the differential cross-section in the forward direction, at $\theta = 0°$, would be 0·311 barns per unit solid angle, which is in very good agreement with the experimental data in Fig. 4.8. Atoji found similar good agreement in the case of TbC_2 for a Tb^{3+} ion in the state $^7F_8$: for YbC_2 the scattering was slightly less than expected for Yb^{3+} in the $^2F_{7/2}$ state and this may indicate that about 17 per cent of the ytterbium atoms are present as the divalent ion Yb^{2+}.

No paramagnetic scattering was detected from CaC_2 YC_2, LaC_2 or LuC_2 and this is what would be expected if the ions present in the carbides were Ca^{2+}, Y^{3+}, La^{3+} and Lu^{3+}.

The rare-earth sesquicarbides, La_2C_3, Ce_2C_3, Pr_2C_3 and Tb_2C_3 have also been studied by Atoji and co-workers.[19] These compounds have a body-centred cubic structure which belongs to the space group $I\bar{4}3d$ and which contains eight molecules in the unit cell. In this structure there are two positional parameters to determine, one for the metal atoms and one for the oxygen atoms, and these were found by applying least-squares analysis methods to the powder data. From the results the C—C distances were calculated. For La_2C_3, Pr_2C_3 and Tb_2C_3 this distance is practically the same in each case, with an average value of 1·238 Å, whereas for Ce_2C_3 it is significantly longer at 1·276 Å. The former distance of 1·238 Å is considerably larger than the C—C distance found above in CaC_2 and definitely shorter than the average C—C distance in the rare-earth dicarbides. The distinctive case of Ce_2C_3 is associated with the fact, as supported by the paramagnetic scattering, that the cerium ion in the sesquicarbide is not in the purely trivalent state. In each of the other sesquicarbides the magnetic scattering is consistent with the assumption that the metal ions are in the pure trivalent Hund ground state. Thus the La^{3+} ion which is in the $^1S_0$ state is diamagnetic, whereas the amount of paramagnetic scattering shown by praseodymium and terbium is what would be expected from the Pr^{3+} ion, which is $^3H_4$, and from Tb^{3+}, which is $^7F_8$. For cerium on the other hand the intensity of the paramagnetic scattering is only about 65 per cent of what would be expected by Ce^{3+} ions which would be in the state $^2F_{5/2}$ which we have already found in the dicarbide. The neutron scattering results for Ce_2C_3 are shown in Fig. 4.9, where the non-agreement with the theoretical curve for a trivalent Ce^{3+} ion contrasts markedly with the good agreement which was found for the dicarbide CeC_2 in Fig. 4.8. It is therefore believed that only 65 per cent of the cerium ions are present as Ce^{3+} and that the remainder occur as Ce^{4+} in the diamagnetic $^1S_0$ state. We may therefore make the same general conclusion for the sesquicarbides as we drew for the dicarbides, namely that the C—C distance increases as the metallic valency increases.

For a more detailed discussion of the relations between the bond lengths, intermetallic separations and the electronic states in both the dicarbides and the sesquicarbides, the reader is referred to the original papers.[16, 19, 33]

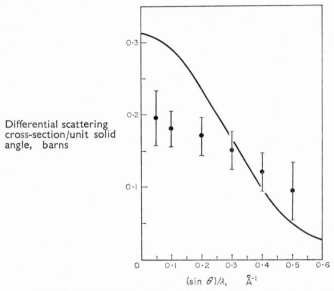

FIG. 4.9. The differential paramagnetic scattering cross-section $d\sigma/d\omega$ for Ce in Ce_2C_3 as measured experimentally. The value of 0·2 barns at $\theta = 0°$ is much below that of 0·31 barns found for Ce^{3+} in CeC_2 and suggests that about 35 per cent of the cerium atoms in Ce_2C_3 are present as diamagnetic Ce^{4+} ions. The full-line is the computed curve for Ce^{3+} ions ($^2F_{5/2}$) using a screening constant s equal to 39. (Atoji and Williams, *J. chem. Phys.* 1961, **35**, 1960.)

The positions of the carbon atoms in austenite have been investigated[20] by Bykov and Vinogradov. Austenite, which consists of metallic iron containing about $1\frac{1}{2}$ atomic per cent of carbon, has a face-centred cubic structure and it is likely that the carbon atoms lie in octahedrally co-ordinated sites, such as $00\frac{1}{2}$, $0\frac{1}{2}0$, $\frac{1}{2}00$ and $\frac{1}{2}\frac{1}{2}\frac{1}{2}$, rather than in tetrahedrally co-ordinated sites such as $\frac{1}{4}\frac{1}{4}\frac{1}{4}$. The scattering amplitude of carbon for neutrons is $0·66 \times 10^{-12}$ compared with $0·96 \times 10^{-12}$ cm for iron but, although this is quite a favourable ratio in comparison with that for X-rays, the contribution from the $1\frac{1}{2}$ per cent of carbon atoms is quite insufficient to discriminate between the octahedral and tetrahedral structures. The problem was solved, however, by weakening the scattering contribution of the metal atoms by diluting the iron with manganese, which has a scattering amplitude of opposite sign. By studying an alloy of composition 1·5 per cent C, 35 per cent Mn and 63·5 per cent Fe it was possible to show that there was good agreement between the observed and calculated intensities for a structure in which the carbon atoms occupied octahedral holes, but not for a tetrahedral type of structure.

An account of some studies of the carbides of titanium and tungsten is given in the following chapter, where these compounds are considered alongside the hydrides with which they are closely related.

4.3. Nitrates, Nitrites and Cyanides

Lead nitrate $PbNO_3$ has been studied[21] by Hamilton at temperatures up to 300°C in a search for evidence in support of the suggestion that the nitrate group is rotating. However, no free rotation is found to occur and it is concluded that the potential barrier for hindered rotation is at least $16kT$. The value of 1·267 Å found for the length of the N—O bond is rather longer than that of 1·22 Å which was reported in early X-ray studies.

A determination of the structural and thermal parameters of the ferroelectric form of $NaNO_2$ by Kay and Frazer[22] takes particular advantage of the fact that neutron scattering is a nuclear effect and independent of the electronic states of the atoms. In $NaNO_2$ there is uncertainty about the electronic distribution of the NO_2 group and, as a result there is doubt about the correct X-ray scattering amplitudes and form-factor curves which should be used for nitrogen and oxygen. The limitation is particularly troublesome when it is desired to determine individual anisotropic temperature factors for each atom. The situation is much more favourable for neutrons because the scattering is isotropic and advantage can be taken of the large neutron scattering amplitude of the nitrogen atom. For X-rays, on the other hand, a positively charged nitrogen atom is a very weak scatterer. Table 4.1 indicates the improved accuracy which was obtained with neutrons in comparison with two earlier[31, 32] X-ray refinements and, as expected, the improvement is particularly noteworthy for the nitrogen atom. The

7

TABLE 4.1

	X-rays	Neutrons
y parameter for sodium	0·5852 ± 0·002[31] 0·5862 ± 0·002[32]	0.5853 ± 0.001
y parameter for nitrogen	0·1217 ± 0·005 0·1188 ± 0·004	0·1200 ± 0·0007
z parameter for oxygen	0·1946 ± 0·003 0·1944 ± 0·002	0·1941 ± 0·0006

neutron parameters were deduced by least-squares analysis from intensity measurements of a set of $0kl$ reflections for a single-crystal at room temperature. Only for the oxygen atoms was any appreciable anisotropy of thermal motion found. The final "discrepancy factor" for the structure analysis reached the very low value of 2·7 per cent. At 158°C there is a phase transition for $NaNO_2$, with loss of its ferro-electric properties, and the crystallographic space group changes from $Im2m$ to $Immm$. The appearance of the extra mirror plane of symmetry means that there is either rotation or disorder among the nitrite groups. A neutron study similar to that just described has been made at 185°C by Kay, Frazer and Ueda.[23] There is no evidence of free rotation and, although there is a possibility of hindered rotation with a high potential barrier, the best agreement with experiment is given by a disordered model.

Single crystals of two inorganic cyanides have been examined, $Hg(CN)_2$ by Hvoslef,[24] and $K_3Co(CN)_6$ by Curry and Runciman.[25] In each case a main aim of the analysis was to determine whether the carbon or nitrogen atom of the cyanide group formed the link with the metal atom, taking advantage of the relatively large neutron scattering amplitudes of C and N, and the fact that the value for nitrogen is substantially the larger of the two. It was established for each compound that it is the *carbon* atom which is attached to the metal atom. In $K_3Co(CN)_6$ each cobalt ion is surrounded by an octahedron of cyanide groups. For two of the three pairs of CN groups the Co—C—N bonds are collinear but there appears to be a slight departure from a straight line for the third pair. In the case of $Hg(CN)_2$ it was concluded that the molecular chain of atoms N—C—Hg—C—N was not quite linear but slightly zig-zag, with interbond angles of about 172°. The lengths of the triple bond C≡N are given as 1·15 and 1·186 ± 0·024 Å respectively for the two compounds.

Much more recently[26] Elliott and Hastings (1961) have examined KCN with neutrons. At room temperature this has a cubic NaCl-type structure and has been examined several times with X-rays.[27, 28, 29] The problem is to try and distinguish between a model in which there is free rotation of the CN⁻ groups and a model in which the CN⁻ groups are randomly directed along body diagonals. In the neutron study the intensities for the rotating model were calculated according to the formula

$$|F|^2 \sim \left[4b_K \pm (4b_C + 4b_N) \frac{\sin x}{x} \right]^2 \qquad (4.3.1)$$

where $x = 4\pi r(\sin \theta)/\lambda$, r is the radius of the rotating group and b_K, b_C, b_N are the scattering lengths of potassium, carbon and nitrogen. The term $\sin x/x$ takes into account the distribution of scattering matter over the volume of space covered by the rotating group. It was found that for a static model no agreement with the observed intensities was possible within a range of 1·06–1·26 Å for the length of the C—N bond. The rotating model, on the other hand, gave good agreement if it was assumed that $r = 0.580$ Å, corresponding to a C—N distance of 1·16 ± 0·01 Å. This would therefore appear to be one of the few compounds in which free rotation of a group seems to take place.

Several of the rare-earth nitrides, which have face-centred cubic structures of the NaCl-type have been examined[30] by Wilkinson et al. These compounds are of interest because of their magnetic properties and we shall discuss them in Chapter 7.

REFERENCES

1. KOEHLER, W. C. and WOLLAN, E. O. *Acta cryst.* 1953, **6**, 741.
2. ZACHARIASEN, W. H. *Z. phys. Chem.* 1926, **123**, 134; and *Z. Krystallogr.* 1929, **70**, 187.
3. PAULING, L. *Z. Krystallogr.* 1928, **69**, 415.
4. MILLIGAN, W. O. *et al.* *J. Phys. Chem.* 1953, **57**, 535.
5. PAULING, L. and SHAPPELL, M. D. *Z. Kristallogr.* 1930, **75**, 128.
6. ANDRESEN, A. F. *Acta cryst.* 1958, **11**, 612.
7. WILLIS, B. T. M. In the press 1962.
8. SCATTURIN, V., BELLON, P. L. and SALKIND, A. J. *Trans. electrochem. Soc.* 1961, **108**, 819.
9. KAY, M. I. *Acta cryst.* 1961, **14**, 80.
10. LECIEJEWICZ, J. *Acta cryst.* 1961, **14**, 66.
11. FRAZER, B. C., DANNER, H. and PEPINSKY, R. *Phys. Rev.* 1955, **100**, 745.
    SHIRANE, G., DANNER, H. and PEPINSKY, R. *Phys. Rev.* 1957, **105**, 856.
12. SHIRANE, G., PEPINSKY, R. and FRAZER, B. C. *Acta cryst.* 1956, **9**, 131.
13. JONA, F., SHIRANE, G., MAZZI, F. and PEPINSKY, R. *Phys. Rev.* 1957, **105**, 849.
14. ATOJI, M. *et al.* *J. Amer. chem. Soc.* 1958, **80**, 1804.
15. ATOJI, M. and MEDRUD, R. C. *J. chem. Phys.* 1959, **31**, 332.

16. ATOJI, M.   *J. chem. Phys.* 1961, **35**, 1950.
17. BACON, G. E.   *Neutron Diffraction* 2nd ed., Chap. VI, Oxford University Press, London, 1962.
18. TRAMMELL, G. T.   *Phys. Rev.* 1953, **92**, 1387.
19. ATOJI, M. and WILLIAMS, D. E.   *J. chem. Phys.* 1961, **35**, 1960.
20. BYKOV, V. N. and VINOGRADOV, S. I.   *Kristallografiya SSSR* 1958, **3**, 304.
21. HAMILTON, W. C.   *Acta cryst.* 1957, **10**, 103.
22. KAY, M. I. and FRAZER, B. C.   *Acta cryst.* 1961, **14**, 56.
23. KAY, M. I., FRAZER, B. C. and UEDA, R.   *J. phys. Soc. Japan* 1962, **17**, Suppl. B-II, 389.
24. HVOSLEF, J.   *Acta chem. Scand.* 1958, **12**, 1568.
25. CURRY, N. A. and RUNCIMAN, W. A.   *Acta cryst.* 1959, **12**, 674.
26. ELLIOTT, N. and HASTINGS, J.   *Acta cryst.* 1961, **14**, 1018.
27. VERWOEL, H. J. and BIJVOET, J. M.   *Z. Kristallogr.* 1938, **100**, 210.
28. BIJVOET, J. M. and LELY, J. A.   *Rec. Trav. chim. Pays-Bas*, 1940, **59**, 908.
29. SIEGEL, L. A.   *J. chem. Phys.* 1949, **17**, 1146.
30. WILKINSON, M. K. *et al.*   *J. Appl. Phys.* 1960, **31**, 358S.
31. TRUTER, M. R.   *Acta cryst.* 1954, **7**, 73.
32. CARPENTER, G. B.   *Acta cryst.* 1955, **8**, 852.
33. ATOJI, M.   *J. phys. Soc. Japan* 1962, **17**, Suppl. B-II, 395.
34. ATOJI, M., GSCHNEIDNER, K., DAANE, A. H., BUNDLE, R. E. and SPEDDING, F. H. *J. Amer. chem. Soc.* 1958, **80**, 1804.

CHAPTER 5

METAL HYDRIDES AND AMMONIUM COMPOUNDS

5.1. Hydrides of Cu, Hf, Ti, Zr, Pd and AlTh$_2$

Before neutron diffraction methods became available, there had been many X-ray and metallographic studies of metal hydrides which revealed the presence of a number of different phases as more and more hydrogen was added to the metal. However, these studies were not able to define the hydrogen positions very accurately and these positions were usually inferred indirectly. Most of these metal-hydrogen phases have simple crystallographic structures and neutron methods, taking advantage of the more substantial scattering amplitude of hydrogen or the very favourable amplitude of deuterium, have been able to elucidate these structures from powder-diffraction patterns. In general the deuterated compounds have been examined.

Typical systems which have been studied, mainly by Sidhu and his co-workers,[1, 2] are those for the metals hafnium, zirconium and titanium. In each case there exists a characteristic single-phase hydride with a face-centred fluorite (CaF$_2$) type of structure. This is, however, always a defect structure, with only a limited fraction of what we may call the "fluorine" sites filled, and there is a transformation to a tetragonal structure before the stoichiometric composition MH$_2$ is reached. In the case of hafnium the face-centred fluorite structure (shown in Fig. 5.1 (i)) exists between the compositions represented approximately by HfD$_{1.62}$ and HfD$_{1.82}$ and it has been studied in detail for HfD$_{1.628}$. Over this range of composition the unit cell dimension remains constant, giving an interatomic Hf—Hf separation of $3 \cdot 309 \pm \cdot 003$ Å, which is a few percent greater than the $3 \cdot 198$ Å which is found in the pure metal. When the hydrogen content exceeds about $64\frac{1}{2}$ atomic per cent (represented by the formula HfD$_{1.82}$) there is a transformation to a face-centred tetragonal structure which has been studied in detail for the composition represented by HfD$_{1.983}$. The distance of closest approach of the metal atoms is reduced to $3 \cdot 270 \pm \cdot 003$ Å and the strengthening of the atomic bonds can be seen by comparing some of the physical

85

properties of hydrides with the two different structures. The zirconium-hydrogen system has not been studied in such detail by neutrons but ZrD_2 has been examined and together with the results of X-ray diffraction studies it seems likely that the system is very similar to the hafnium-hydrogen system. A full study of titanium hydrides and deuterides has shown the occurrence of similar phases to those found for hafnium but it appears that the face-centred cubic phase extends over a much wider range of composition and does not transform to the tetragonal phase as readily as in the other two systems. Thus the composition

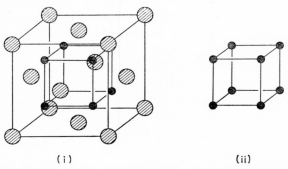

(i)   (ii)

Fig. 5.1. (i) Shows the face-centred cubic unit cell of $HfD_{1.628}$. The large shaded atoms are hafnium and the deuterium atoms occupy some of the fluorite type positions indicated by the small filled circles. At higher concentrations of deuterium there is a slight distortion to tetragonal symmetry.

If the hafnium atoms are replaced by a mixture of titanium and zirconium in the ratio 62 : 38 then they are "invisible" so far as coherent reflections are concerned. At the composition MD_2 the effective unit cell is then that shown at (ii), which may be considered as pure deuterium having a slightly distorted simple cubic cell.

$TiD_{1.971}$ is still cubic and some of its physical properties suggest that it is more strongly bound than its counterpart $HfD_{1.828}$. In all of these compounds it appears that the hydrogen must exist as an ion, having lost an electron, since the size of the holes which it occupies is too small to accommodate atoms.

These conclusions about the hydrogen positions in the hafnium, titanium and zirconium hydrides have been supported very elegantly by Sidhu's studies[2] with so-called "null matrices". A typical example is the deuterium compound $MD_{1.99}$ where the metal M represents a disordered mixture of 62 atomic per cent of titanium and 38 atomic per cent of zirconium. The reason for the choice of this particular alloy-composition is that the scattering amplitudes of titanium and zirconium are -0.38, $+0.62 \times 10^{-12}$ cm respectively, so that their respective contributions to the coherent diffraction peaks of the alloy are equal and opposite: thus the "atoms" of $Ti_{0.62}Zr_{0.38}$ are invisible. This is demonstrated very clearly in Fig. 5.2 which compares the X-ray and neutron diffraction patterns of the alloy with those of pure zirconium and titanium. As expected, the neutron pattern of the alloy shows no Bragg reflections, but a high isotropic background of scattering. If we now consider the tetragonal distorted-fluorite compound

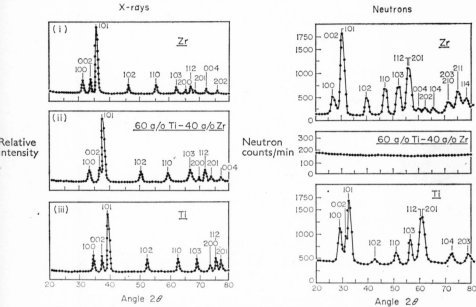

FIG. 5.2. A comparison of, left, X-ray diffraction patterns at $\lambda = 1 \cdot 54$ Å and, right, the neutron patterns at $\lambda = 1 \cdot 26$ Å for (i) zirconium (ii) an alloy of 60 per cent Ti with 40 per cent Zr and (iii) titanium. The neutron pattern of the alloy shows no coherent spectra. (Sidhu et al. J. Appl. Phys. 1959, 30, 1323.)

$MD_{1.99}$ made by using this alloy instead of a pure metal we shall expect the diffraction pattern to be due simply to the deuterium atoms. Calculation shows that the only reflections to be expected are those for which h, k, l are all even, since the deuterium atoms lie on a simple cubic unit cell of half size. This is shown very clearly in Fig. 5.3 which compares the pattern of the "invisible alloy" deuteride with the patterns of $ZrD_{1.95}$ and $TiD_{1.98}$. The middle pattern in this figure is identical with what would be given by a slightly distorted form of simple-cubic deuterium, as sketched in Fig. 5.1 (ii), for which the unit cell dimension is equal to a half of the value for MD_2.

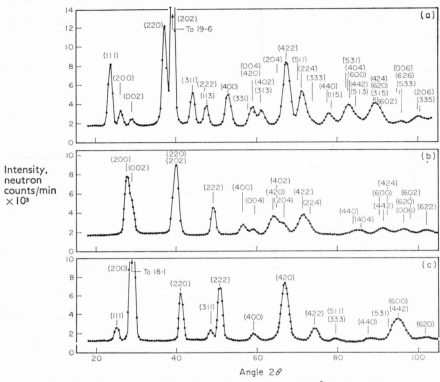

Intensity,
neutron
counts/min
× 10³

Angle 2θ

Fig. 5.3. The neutron diffraction patterns at $\lambda = 1\cdot09$ Å for (a) $ZrD_{1\cdot95}$, (b) $MD_{1\cdot99}$, where M is 62 per cent Ti—38 per cent Zr, and (c) $Ti\ D_{1\cdot98}$. The alloy M in (b) is effectively invisible with the result that the apparent unit cell is of half size (as drawn in Fig. 5.1 (ii)) and only reflections for which h, k, l are all even now appear. (Sidhu *et al.*, *J. Appl. Phys.* 1959, **30**, 1323.)

A very similar study has been made of the *carbides* of titanium and tungsten, which form extended solid solutions, and which can be mentioned conveniently here in view of their close relation to the hydrides. The scattering amplitude of tungsten is $0\cdot47 \times 10^{-12}$ cm, rather lower than for zirconium, and the alloy composition which will produce "invisible" metal atoms is 55 atomic per cent of titanium with 45 per cent of tungsten. The carbides have an NaCl type of structure so that the only reflections which appear are those for which h, k, l are all even or all odd and the structure amplitude factors are $4(b_C + b_M)$, $4(b_C - b_M)$ respectively in the two cases. For the alloy carbide $Ti_{0\cdot55}\ W_{0\cdot45}C$ the structure factor for the unit cell reduces in all cases to $4b_C$, i.e. four times the scattering length of a carbon atom. The observed pattern, which is the lower curve in Fig. 5.4, contrasts markedly with the upper curve for

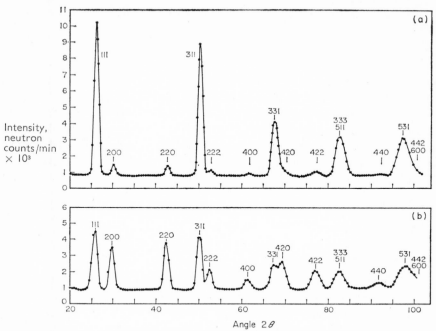

FIG. 5.4. A comparison of the neutron diffraction patterns ($\lambda = 1\cdot09$ Å), for (a) TiC and (b) MC where M is an "invisible" mixture of 55 atomic per cent of titanium with 45 atomic per cent of tungsten. For (b) the effective structure is a face-centred cubic form of carbon. (Sidhu *et al.* *J. Appl. Phys.* 1959, **30**, 1323.)

titanium carbide in which the "all odd" reflections are intense and the "all even" ones are weak. In effect the lower curve is the diffraction pattern which would be given by a face-centred cubic form of carbon. It must be emphasised that these null-matrix methods can only be used when the two metal atoms in the solid solution remain randomly distributed. If ordering takes place, as for example is found in the case of $MD_{1\cdot2}$, then the metal atoms will no longer be invisible and will contribute to the coherent diffraction peaks.

The results of a very interesting study[3] of the palladium-hydrogen system by Worsham, Wilkinson and Shull throw light on the mechanism of the catalytic activity of palladium in hydrogenation processes. Previously X-ray studies had shown that two face-centred cubic phases occurred in the Pd-H system, depending on the amount of hydrogen present. At low concentrations the α-phase exists, with a unit cell dimension of 3·89 Å which is almost identical with that of pure palladium. With further increase of hydrogen concentration a β-phase is produced, with its unit cell dimension expanded to 4·02 Å, and at normal temperature and pressure saturation is reached when the atomic ratio H/Pd has risen to 0·7. The neutron diffraction data show that in this phase the hydrogen atoms are randomly distributed among the octahedral positions of the face-centred cubic lattice, thus forming what we may describe as an NaCl-type structure in which the chlorine positions are only 70 per cent filled. The details of this structure can be established quantitatively from a comparison of the powder-diffraction pattern of pure palladium with those of the hydrogenated and deuterated samples which have the compositions $PdH_{0.706}$ and $PdD_{0.658}$. These three patterns are illustrated in Fig. 5.5. Comparison of the pattern for $PdD_{0.658}$ with that of pure Pd shows the increase of intensity for reflections with all-even indices and a reduction for all-odd indices which is characteristic of the NaCl type of structure. For $PdH_{0.706}$ the reverse changes occur, because of the fact that palladium and hydrogen have scattering amplitudes which are of opposite sign. The greatly reduced background in the top curve, compared with the centre one, illustrates the great advantage of using deuterated materials when powder-diffraction patterns have to be employed. Calculation of the expected intensities for the measured volume of gas which the metal has absorbed shows that the whole of the hydrogen enters these octahedral positions and only a negligible amount is available for a "rift network" —a conception which had been previously advanced, according to which the hydrogen was not located in the palladium lattice but merely distributed through the bulk metal as if in a state of extensive surface adsorption.

Measurements of the total scattering cross-section of the hydrogen in the palladium compounds showed that it was abnormally low, amounting to only 29 barns instead of the more usual value of about 38 barns for bound atoms in normal hydrogen-containing compounds. It appears therefore that the hydrogen remains relatively free and that although the hydrogen gas is dissociated into atoms located on the octahedral sites, any bonds formed between the hydrogen and palladium atoms are unusually weak. The catalytic activity in hydrogenation would therefore seem to be due to the ability of the β-phase compound to furnish single atoms of hydrogen.

A study of the diffraction patterns was also made at compositions corresponding to $PdH_{0.064}$ and $PdD_{0.075}$. Even at these low concentrations it appeared that at least half of the hydrogen was present as the β phase, with the same NaCl-type structure and the expanded

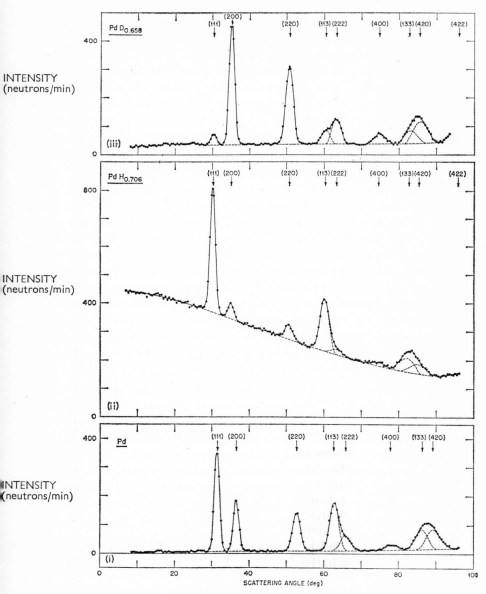

FIG. 5.5. The change in the diffraction pattern (i) of palladium when (ii) hydrogen or (iii) deuterium is introduced: the hydrogen and deuterium atoms occupy octahedral positions in the palladium unit cell, thus tending to produce a structure of the NaCl-type. (Worsham *et al. J. Phys. Chem. Solids*, 1957, **3**, 303.)

unit cell of side 4·02 Å. It was not found possible to determine whether the few hydrogen atoms which were contained in the α phase occupied any particular crystallographic positions within the unit cell.

More recently Bergsma and Goedkoop[4] have studied single crystals of palladium and confirmed the conclusions about PdH which were arrived at from the powder data. Moreover their work showed that when the palladium took up hydrogen electrolytically it had the same NaCl-type of structure as was produced by gaseous absorption, a matter on which there had been some earlier speculation. From the neutron intensities it was found that the root-mean-square amplitudes of thermal motion for the palladium and hydrogen atoms were 0·10, 0·24 Å respectively. A study was also made of the energy changes when a beam of "cold" neutrons, with an incident energy of 0·004 eV, was scattered. From these measurements it was concluded that the vibrational energy of the proton was 0·056 eV which leads to a calculated root-mean-square displacement, relative to the palladium atoms, of 0·22 Å which is in agreement with the conclusions from the data for coherent elastic scattering.

Bergsma, Goedkoop and Van Vucht[5] have examined the take-up of deuterium by the intermetallic compound $AlTh_2$. The tetragonal symmetry of $AlTh_2$ is preserved up to the ultimate composition $AlTh_2D_4$. When the unit cell dimensions c, a are plotted against the deuterium content it is found that c increases steadily but a increases only up to the composition which includes two atoms of hydrogen, at which there is a sharp break in the curve followed by a decrease up to the stage when saturation is reached. The neutron powder-diffraction patterns suggest that at $AlTh_2D_4$ there is complete filling of a set of 16-fold positions in the original unit cell, which contains four "molecules" of $AlTh_2$. The main features of the structure are indicated in Fig. 5.6, where the thorium and aluminium atoms in the projection lie in alternate layers perpendicular to the c-axis, each separated by $c/4$. The thorium atoms form distorted tetrahedra, having three atoms in one layer (say at $z = 0$) and a fourth atom in the layer $c/2$ above (at $z = c/2$ in the figure). In the deuterides the deuterium atoms occupy roughly the centres of these tetrahedra, which occur in pairs sharing a common base such as ABC and pointing one up and one down to P and P'. It is believed that up to the composition $AlThD_2$ one tetrahedron in each pair has a deuterium atom occupying its centre and the neutron data suggest that the two alternative positions are filled at random, with no correlation between the mode of filling of neighbouring pairs of tetrahedra. Beyond this composition, where the a dimension changes discontinuously, additional uptake of deuterium must result in both tetrahedra in the pairs becoming steadily filled. The arrangement of thorium and deuterium atoms in the final staturated compound $AlTh_2D_4$ is quite similar to that found in ThD_2 which is discussed later. All the neutron observations with the $AlTh_2$ system were made using the deuterides, rather than the normal hydrides, in order to avoid the very high incoherent scattering of hydrogen in the powder samples.

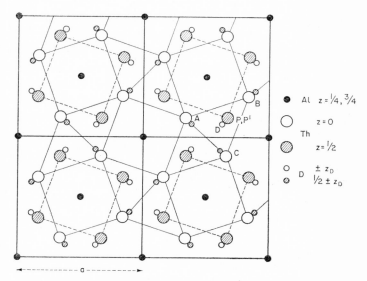

Fig. 5.6. A view of the structure of $AlTh_2D_n$ seen along the c-axis. The thorium atoms form tetrahedra sharing a common base, such as ABC, and pointing up and down respectively to a vertex at P ($z = \frac{1}{2}$) or its counterpart P' ($z = -\frac{1}{2}$). The positions for the deuterium atoms are near the centres of these tetrahedra at D, D', above or below ABC at random. (After Bergsma, Goedkoop and Van Vucht, *Acta cryst.* 1961, **14**, 223.)

Goedkoop and Andresen[6] have studied copper hydride, a rather dubious precipitate produced by interaction of solutions of hypophosphorous acid and copper sulphate and to which two alternative structures had been assigned in 1926. The neutron study of both the normal and deuterated compounds supported the hexagonal wurzite structure suggested by Muller and Bradley.[7] It would not however appear to be established that CuH is a stoichiometric compound, like LiH and NaH, and it may well be that it is a defect structure, like the hydrogen compounds of the other heavier metals which we have been discussing.

5.2. Heavy-metal Hydrides

In some early studies of heavy-metal hydrides Rundle, Shull and Wollan[8] have examined ThH_2, ThD_2 and ZrD_2, and Rundle[9] has examined UD_3, in each case using powder-diffraction patterns. The dihydrides were found to have distorted fluorite structures which can be regarded as produced by compressing the cubic CaF_2 structure along one axis to produce a structure with tetragonal symmetry and having the c axis smaller than a. For zirconium hydride the metal-hydrogen separation agrees with predictions but for thorium hydride it is unusually large.

A similar anomaly of an unexpectedly large metal–hydrogen distance appears in Rundle's structure for UD_3. One aim of this work was to investigate the possible existence of a "bridge" structure in which the hydrogen atoms served to bond together pairs of uranium atoms, but this suggestion was found to be incompatible with the neutron data. In the favoured model there are two types of uranium atom, surrounded by two different arrangements of twelve hydrogen atoms but with U–D distances of 2·32 Å in each case. Using Pauling's value of 1·52 Å for the radius of uranium in twelve-fold coordination this leaves 0·80 Å for the radius of the hydrogen atoms and this is about three times as large as would be expected.

5.3. Alkali Metal and Alkaline-earth Hydrides

Sodium hydride and deuteride were among the earliest compounds to be studied by neutrons and they were shown[10] by Shull *et al.* (1948), who examined their powder patterns, to have the sodium chloride type of structure. Much more recently a very detailed examination of single crystals of lithium hydride by both X-rays and neutrons has been made.[11] An experimental study of this compound is of particular interest because the two atoms together contain only four electrons and there is some prospect of calculating the electron density distribution theoretically with sufficient accuracy to compare it with what is inferred by X-ray diffraction. The contribution made by the neutron data is to permit an assessment of the amplitudes of thermal vibration independently of any assumptions concerning atomic scattering factors, fixing unambiguously the thermal motion of the nuclei. In this work the vibration amplitudes of the lithium and hydrogen atoms were both first determined from the values of the integrated intensities of the coherent

Bragg reflections for neutrons. A very valuable check on the amplitude found for hydrogen was then made by measuring the elastic part of the spin-incoherent scattering due to hydrogen. Unlike the *total* spin incoherent scattering, the elastic component falls off with angle according to the expression $\exp\left(-2B_H(\sin\, ^2\theta)/\lambda^2\right)$, where B_H is the Debye factor for hydrogen, and this component can be measured separately by reflecting the initially-scattered beam by means of a second crystal. This "analysing crystal" is set to reflect into the measuring counter only those neutrons which have not undergone any change in wavelength when scattered by the lithium hydride. Very convincing agreement was achieved between the values of B_H given by these two different methods. The X-ray data can then be used to suggest, first, that the ionic charges on the lithium and hydrogen ions are between 0·8 and 1·0 and, secondly, that the lithium ion is largely unaffected by the crystalline field but there is a marked contraction of the hydrogen ions. The extent of this contraction is approximately equal to that calculated by Waller and Lundqvist[12] and by Hurst.[13]

A study of powdered samples of calcium hydride and deuteride has resulted in a reassessment[24] of the positions of the hydrogen atoms.

5.4. Ammonium Halides

Ammonium fluoride, NH_4F, has a wurtzite structure in which each nitrogen atom is surrounded by a tetrahedron of fluorine atoms, with strong hydrogen bonds between N and F. In the other ammonium halides, however, the situation is much more complicated and several different phases exist. They may be summarized as follows, and the types of crystal structure which have been proposed from the location of the nitrogen and halogen atoms by X-rays are indicated in brackets.

NH_4Cl	Phase I (NaCl type)	$\xleftrightarrow{184\cdot3°C}$	Phase II (CsCl)	$\xleftrightarrow{-30\cdot5°C}$	Phase III (CsCl)	
ND_4Cl	Phase I (NaCl)	$\xleftrightarrow{175°C}$	Phase II (CsCl)	$\xleftrightarrow{-23\cdot8°C}$	Phase III (CsCl)	
NH_4Br	Phase I (NaCl)	$\xleftrightarrow{137\cdot8°C}$	Phase II (CsCl)	$\xleftrightarrow{-38\cdot1°C}$	Phase III tetragonal distorted (CsCl)	
ND_4Br	Phase I (NaCl)	$\xleftrightarrow{125°C}$	Phase II (CsCl)	$\xleftrightarrow{-58\cdot4°C}$	Phase III tetragonal	$\xleftrightarrow{-104°C}$ Phase IV (CsCl)
NH_4I	Phase I (NaCl)	$\xleftrightarrow{-17\cdot6°C}$	Phase II (CsCl)	$\xleftrightarrow{-41\cdot6°C}$	Phase III tetragonal	

The positions of the hydrogen atoms in these compounds have been studied by Levy and Peterson,[14, 15, 16] in a lengthy series of investigations, in order to elucidate the details of the phase changes. The most detailed work[16] has been carried out with powdered samples of ND_4Br for which all four phases have been examined and the results for this compound are summarized in Fig. 5.7. In the low-temperature form, Phase IV, the bromine and ND_4^+ ions occupy the normal Cs, Cl positions in the CsCl structure and the ND_4 ions lie in the same orientation throughout the structure. Each bromine atom is tetrahedrally surrounded by deuterium atoms. This same simple structure is also found for the lowest temperature modifications of NH_4Cl and ND_4Cl. In Phase III of ND_4Br the ND_4^+ ions again lie in parallel columns, along the c-axis, but neighbouring columns are oppositely oriented (Fig. 5.7C). The a axis is greater than c by a factor of $\sqrt{2}$ and the unit cell contains two molecules, but there is a pseudo-cell which is indicated by the dotted lines in the figure and which makes clear the relation of the tetragonal Phase III to the CsCl structure of Phase IV. It is believed that this same Phase III structure is correct for NH_4I and NH_4Br also.

Phase II of ND_4Br includes two different orientations of the ND_4^+ ions which occur at random to give a disordered structure (Fig. 5.7B), and this structure seems to be common to Phase II of all these halides. For the chlorides and bromides it is the structure which exists at room temperature and had earlier been the subject of much speculation. It was at one time thought that the ammonium ions rotated more or less freely but the neutron measurements established quite conclusively that this was not the case and that there was a random distribution of the two possible orientations of the ions. It was also concluded that the thermal motions of the ions consisted of a rotatory oscillation over a cone defined by a half-angle of about $12°$.

The detailed structure of the high-temperature phase of the halides has proved the most difficult to determine. An ordered orientation of the ND_4^+ groups would not be compatible with the full symmetry: at the same time the neutron data rule out the possibility that the ND_4 groups rotate freely. The three possible models which satisfy the experimental data are illustrated at D, E and F in Fig. 5.7. In D one one of the four N-D bonds is directed towards one (chosen at random) of the six surrounding halogen ions and the ND_4^+ group rotates about this bond. In model E there is no rotation and two of the four deuterium atoms get as close as they mutually can to two halogen atoms: in model F three of the four deuterium atoms achieve near approaches. The neutron data agree equally well with each model but infra-red measurements support the model shown at D where there is rotation about a single axis.

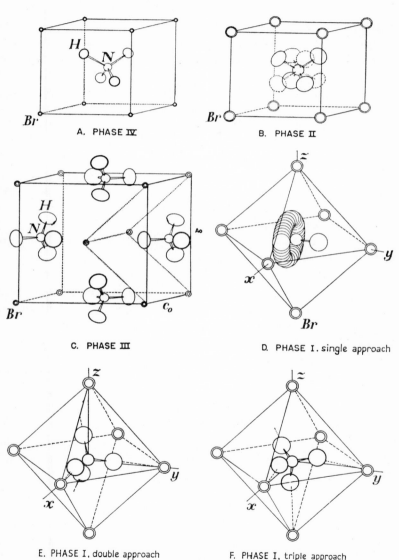

A. PHASE IV

B. PHASE II

C. PHASE III

D. PHASE I. single approach

E. PHASE I, double approach

F. PHASE I, triple approach

FIG. 5.7. Diagrams of the structures proposed for the four phases of ND_4Br by Levy and Peterson. (Reproduced from *Neutron Diffraction*, Bacon, Oxford University Press.)

For all the phases of ND_4Br the nitrogen–deuterium distance was found to be 1.03 ± 0.02 Å. It may be noted that in no case, either for the bromide or any of the other halides, is there any evidence of *free* rotation of the ammonium ion.

Much more recently Smith and Levy[17] have studied ammonium perchlorate, NH_4ClO_4, at room temperature, for which an ordered hydrogen-bonded arrangement of the ammonium ions had been suggested from the X-ray study of Venkatesan. However, the neutron data are not consistent with this and Fourier projections show no more than a smeared out distribution of negative scattering density around the nitrogen atom. This indicates either some static disordered arrangement of the ammonium ions or else a rotation of these ions. The environment of the NH_4^+ ion in the crystal, with eight oxygen atoms between 2.94 and 3.08 Å and four others between 3.25 and 3.52 Å, makes it seem unlikely that the tetrahedral ion should be static. Measurements of other physical properties, such as the infrared[19] and nuclear magnetic resonance spectra,[20, 21] all favour the possibility that there is free, or almost free, rotation of the ammonium ion in this compound.

Palevsky[22] has recently described the application of a new technique to the study of the motion of atoms and molecular groups. When a beam of long wavelength neutrons passes through a solid there will be no coherent diffraction peaks if the wavelength is greater than twice the maximum interplanar spacing d_{max} in the crystal, because there is then no value of the Bragg angle θ which will satisfy the equation $\lambda = 2d \sin \theta$. The value of $\sin \theta$ would need to be greater than unity. Under these circumstances it becomes particularly easy to observe processes of "inelastic" scattering, in which the incoming neutron exchanges energy with the molecular (and other) vibrations in the crystal. The neutron gains energy, which can be assessed by studying the peaks in the energy spectrum of the scattered neutrons. In this way Palevsky has studied vibrations in ammonium halides. A complementary technique involving energy *loss* has been applied by Venkataraman *et al.*[25]

5.5. Solid Hydrogen and Deuterium

The present chapter on hydrides and ammonium compounds is probably the most convenient place at which to mention a neutron-diffraction study of solid hydrogen and deuterium by Ozerov, Zhdanov and Cogan.[23] The measurements were made at $10°K$ and showed that the two solids were not isomorphous. Both have tetragonal unit cells, but for hydrogen $a = 4\cdot5$, $c = 3\cdot6$ Å giving $c/a = 0\cdot81$ whereas for deuterium $a = 3\cdot4$ and $c = 5\cdot6$ Å giving $c/a = 1\cdot66$. The volume of the unit cell, which contains two molecules, and the nearest-neighbour distances are approximately the same in each case. Certain reflections were observed for which the sum of the h, k, l indices is odd, and which are therefore forbidden for body-centred structures of identical particles. It was suggested that there is ordering of the *ortho-* and *para-*molecules among the atomic sites and that these two types of molecule have different coherent scattering amplitudes.

REFERENCES

1. SIDHU, S. S., LE ROY HEATON and ZAUBERIS, D. D.   *Acta cryst.* 1956, **9**, 607.
2. SIDHU, S. S., LE ROY HEATON and MUELLER, M. H.   *J. Appl. Phys.* 1959, **30**, 1323.
3. WORSHAM, J. E., WILKINSON, M. K. and SHULL, C. G.   *J. Phys. Chem. Solids,* 1957, **3**, 303.
4. BERGSMA, J. and GOEDKOOP, J. A.   *Physica,* 1960, **26**, 744.
5. BERGSMA, J., GOEDKOOP, J. A. and VAN VUCHT, J. H. N.   *Acta cryst.* 1961, **14**, 223.
6. GOEDKOOP, J. A. and ANDRESEN, A. F.   *Acta cryst.* 1955, **8**, 118.
7. MÜLLER, H. and BRADLEY, A. J.   *J. chem. Soc.* 1926, p. 1669.
8. RUNDLE, R. E., SHULL, C. G. and WOLLAN, E. O.   *Acta cryst.* 1952, **5**, 22.
9. RUNDLE, R. E.   *J. Amer. chem. Soc.* 1951, **73**, 4172.
10. SHULL, C. G., WOLLAN, E. O., MORTON, G. A. and DAVIDSON, W. L.   *Phys. Rev.* 1948, **73**, 842.
11. CALDER, R. S., COCHRAN, W., GRIFFITHS, D. and LOWDE, R. D.   *J. Phys. Chem. Solids,* 1962, **23**, 621.
12. WALLER, I. and LUNDQVIST, S. O.   *Ark. Fys.* 1953, **7**, 121.
13. HURST, R. P.   *Phys. Rev.* 1959, **114**, 746.
14. LEVY, H. A. and PETERSON, S. W.   *Phys. Rev.* 1952, **86**, 766.
15. LEVY, H. A. and PETERSON, S. W.   *J. chem. Phys.* 1953, **21**, 366.
16. LEVY, H. A. and PETERSON, S. W.   *J. Amer. chem. Soc.* 1953, **75**, 1536.
17. SMITH, H. G. and LEVY, H. A.   *Acta cryst.* 1962, **15**, 1201.
18. VENKATESAN, K.   *Proc. Ind. Acad. Sci.* 1957, **46A**, 134.
19. WADDINGTON, T. C.   *J. chem. Soc.* 1958, p. 4340.
20. IBERS, J. A.   *J. chem. Phys.* 1960, **32**, 1448.
21. RICHARDS, R. E. and SCHAEFER, T.   *Trans. Faraday Soc.* 1961, **57**, 210.
22. PALEVSKY, H.   *J. Phys. Soc. Japan,* 1962, **17**, Suppl. B-II, 367.
23. OZEROV, R. P., ZHDANOV, G. S. and COGAN, V. S.   *J. Phys. Soc. Japan,* 1962, **17**, Suppl. B-II, 385.
24. BERGSMA, J. and LOOPSTRA, B. O.   *Acta cryst.* 1962, **15**, 92.
25. VENKATARAMAN, G. *et al.*   Symposium on Inelastic Scattering of Neutrons, Chalk River, Canada, 1962.

CHAPTER 6

COMPOUNDS WHICH INCLUDE NEIGHBOURING ELEMENTS

6.1. Introduction

We aim to describe in this chapter some structural studies of compounds which include a pair of elements, usually metals, which are so close together in the Periodic Classification that they cannot be distinguished by X-rays, except by extremely careful measurements of intensities with radiations of specially chosen wavelength. Often, but not always, the neutron scattering amplitudes of these neighbouring elements are considerably different and they can therefore be distinguished from one another by quite rough measurements of intensity. A typical series of elements, and one which is very important in practice, is that of the iron group of transition metals V, Cr, Mn, Fe and Co which have the very varied selection of scattering amplitudes indicated by -0.05, 0.35, -0.36, 0.96 and 0.25×10^{-12} cm and are therefore easily distinguished from each other. On the other hand, even with neutrons iron is difficult to distinguish from nickel, which has a scattering amplitude of 1.03×10^{-12} cm, though in principle a distinction could easily be made in this case if separated isotopes of the two elements were available. The scattering amplitudes of Fe^{57} and Ni^{62}, for example, are 0.23 and -0.87×10^{-12} cm respectively, so that these particular isotopes of the two metals would be easy to distinguish.

6.2. Alloys of Transition Metals

As might be expected, many neutron diffraction studies which take advantage of these differences of scattering amplitude concern alloys of the transition elements and are of metallurgical interest. In particular, it is often quite easy to study the way in which the degree of chemical ordering varies with the nature of the heat treatment which has been employed in the preparation of an alloy. A typical example is provided by Fig. 6.1 which shows the neutron diffraction patterns of two different samples of iron–cobalt alloy of the equiatomic composition FeCo.

In the annealed alloy not only do the normal reflections (such as 110, 200, 211) corresponding to a body-centred cubic structure appear, but there are also quite intense superlattice reflections, such as 100, 111 and 210. The presence of these latter reflections indicates that the structure is very highly ordered, so that most of the iron atoms occupy the corners of the unit cells and the cobalt atoms are at the centres of the cells. When the alloy is quenched, however, this ordering does not occur to any very large extent and the superlattice reflections are only very weak, as in the upper curve of Fig. 6.1. The superlattice reflections are

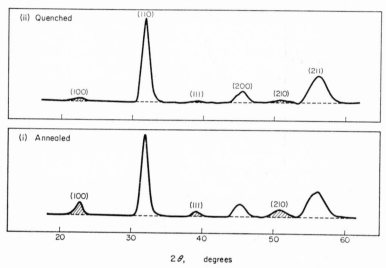

FIG. 6.1. A comparison of the neutron-diffraction patterns of (i) annealed and (ii) quenched samples of FeCo containing 2 per cent of vanadium. The enhancement of the superlattice lines 100, 111 and 210 in the annealed material is due to the increase of the long-range ordering of the Fe and Co atoms at the corners and body-centres respectively of the unit cell.

visible in the neutron diffraction pattern of the ordered annealed alloy because of the relatively large difference between the neutron scattering amplitudes of Fe, Co: for X-ray scattering the two amplitudes are so nearly equal that the superlattice lines from this alloy would not be distinguishable.

For other alloys of the transition elements the neutron data may be of value in indicating that practically no chemical ordering of the two components takes place. An example is provided by the copper-manganese system which has been studied[1, 2] quite extensively because of its interesting magnetic properties. These alloys have a face-centred

tetragonal structure which is a slight distortion of the cubic face-centred
structure of copper. As the proportion of copper in the alloy is increased the intensity of the nuclear reflections such as 200 decreases,
as illustrated in Fig. 6.2, becoming almost zero for alloys containing
30 per cent of copper. The reason for this is that the scattering amplitudes of copper and manganese are of opposite sign, equal to 0·79 and
—0·36 × 10^{-12} cm respectively, and the mean value of the scattering
amplitude for the metal atoms at the composition $Cu_{0.3}Mn_{0.7}$ is practically zero. The fact that the neutron intensities are found to be very

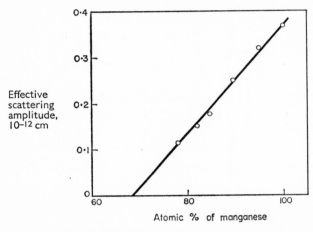

Fig. 6.2. The experimentally-measured nuclear scattering amplitude in
Cu–Mn alloys as a function of the atomic percentage of manganese,
together with the linear relation which would be expected for a random
distribution of the two types of atom.

small for an alloy of this composition indicates therefore that there is a
random arrangement of copper and manganese atoms among the corner
and face-centred sites in the structure, so that it is indeed the *mean*
scattering amplitude which determines the intensities of all the nuclear
reflections.

Not in all cases, however, are conditions favourable for detecting
order in alloys with neutrons. A contrasting example is provided by the
alloy Cu_3Au which can be obtained in a highly-ordered form, with the
copper and gold atoms occupying the face-centre and corner positions
respectively in the cubic unit cell. This order can be demonstrated very
easily with X-rays but it escapes detection with neutrons[3] because the
scattering amplitudes of copper and gold for neutrons happen to be
almost identical.

Some rather similar studies have been made of the degree of order in σ-phase alloys. These alloys between transition elements of the iron group are of technical importance in relation to the physical properties of steels and they have been extensively studied[4, 5] with X-rays. Although the locations of the 30 atomic sites in the unit cell have been found very accurately it is not possible to be certain of the distribution of the component atoms among them, because these atoms have almost equal scattering amplitudes for X-rays. It is found that the atomic parameters of various binary σ phases among the iron group of transition elements are closely similar and we may take as a quite typical example the values for Co–Cr. The space group is $P4/mnm$ and there are five crystallographically-different kinds of atoms which are present in quantities and positions as follows:

Type	I	2 (b)		
	II	4 (f)	$x = 0.103$	
	III	8 (i)	$x = 0.371,$	$y = 0.037$
	IV	8 (i)	$x = 0.566,$	$y = 0.240$
	V	8 (j)	$x = 0.316,$	$y = 0.250,$

using the nomenclature of the International Tables for X-ray Crystallography.[6]

Kasper and Waterstrat[7] have used neutron diffraction to determine the allocation of the two types of atom among these five types of site for the three σ phases Ni–V, Fe–V, and Mn–Cr. The success of their investigation can be realized by considering the results for the nickel–vanadium alloys. These are particularly favourable alloys to study with neutrons, since nickel has a very large scattering length, 1.03×10^{-12} cm, in marked contrast to that of vanadium which is practically zero, being -0.05×10^{-12} cm. In Fig. 6.3 we compare the neutron diffraction patterns for each of the alloys $Ni_{13}V_{17}$, $Ni_{11}V_{19}$ and Ni_9V_{21} with a typical X-ray pattern for a σ phase alloy. The great difference between this X-ray pattern and the neutron patterns proves immediately that there must be considerable ordering of the Ni and V atoms among the five different types of site. This conclusion follows from the fact that the neutron pattern is essentially determined by the distribution of the nickel atoms alone, because the vanadium atoms are practically invisible. If, therefore, the nickel atoms were distributed at random then the neutron pattern would be the same as the pattern for X-rays, since X-rays are not able to make any distinction between the nickel and vanadium atoms. It is possible to make some deductions

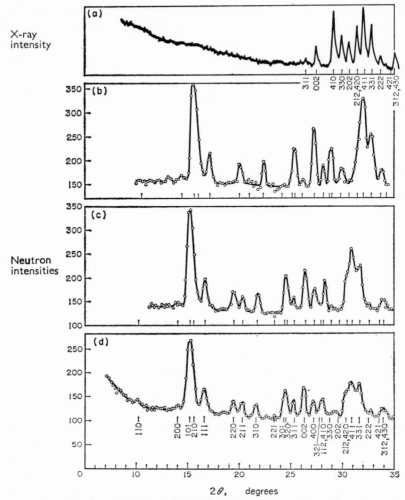

FIG. 6.3. A typical X-ray diffraction pattern of a σ phase alloy, shown at (a) for the Mn–Cr σ phase, is contrasted with the completely different distribution of intensity in the neutron patterns (b), (c), and (d). These neutron patterns are for the σ phases $Ni_{13}V_{17}$, $Ni_{11}V_{19}$ and Ni_9V_{21} respectively. (Kasper and Waterstrat, *Acta cryst.* 1956, **9**, 289.)

about the type of ordering by considering the relative intensities of neutron reflections with various indices. In this way it was concluded that sites of types I and IV were essentially all filled by nickel, whereas those of types II and V were all filled by vanadium. The remaining atoms of either kind occupied sites of Type III.

In a similar way it was demonstrated that there was also ordering in the Fe–V and Mn–Cr systems and a general pattern of ordering could be observed in the three systems. Broadly, it appeared that the iron group elements could be divided into two classes A and B according as they are to the left of manganese in the Periodic Classification (as for V, Cr and also for Mo) or to the right (as for Fe, Co, Ni). The behaviour of manganese itself appears to be anomalous. It was found that, in general, sites of Types I and IV were occupied by Type B atoms and sites of Type II were occupied by Type A atoms: on the other hand there was mixed occupancy of sites of Types III and V.

This kind of investigation has been extended to the study of some ternary phase alloys of Fe–Cr–Mn and Fe–V–Mn by Bykov et al.[8] The particular compositions chosen were Fe 20%, V 25%, Mn 55% and Fe 17%, Cr 27% and Mn 56%, each of which corresponds to a "null matrix" in which the mean scattering amplitude of the metal atoms is approximately zero. The neutron diffraction patterns of these samples showed no coherent reflections, indicating that the different metals were indeed distributed randomly among the possible atomic sites and that there was no significant amount of ordering.

6.3. Spinel Structures

Spinel structures have been very extensively studied with neutrons on account of the fact that the ferrites, which are of very great interest for their magnetic properties, have this kind of structure. The contribution which the examination with neutrons has made to our knowledge of these substances has been two-fold, arising not only from the ability of neutrons to detect magnetic moments but also because they can distinguish between atoms of neighbouring atomic number. The examination[9] of the mineral spinel itself, $MgAl_2O_4$, provides a very good example of the way in which neutrons can discriminate between neighbouring atoms, in this case the ions Mg^{2+}, Al^{3+} which have the same electronic structure and are not distinguishable by X-rays.

The spinel structure belongs to the cubic space group $Fd3m$ and each unit cell contains eight molecules of the general form XY_2O_4 where X and Y are divalent and trivalent metals respectively. The structure forms a very nearly class-packed assembly of oxygen atoms with metal atoms occupying some of the interstices. These interstices are of two types, as can be seen in Fig. 6.4 which is a projection of half of a unit cell. There are eight so-called "A sites" which are each tetrahedrally coordinated by four oxygen atoms and there are sixteen "B sites" which are each octahedrally co-ordinated by six oxygen atoms. The diagram in Fig. 6.5 illustrates more plainly the different co-ordination of the two types of site in three dimensions. The main problem in the examination of an individual spinel compound is to determine the allocation of the X and Y ions among the A and B sites: the other aim is to distinguish small departures in the positions of the oxygen atoms from a proper close-packed arrangement, as represented by deviations of

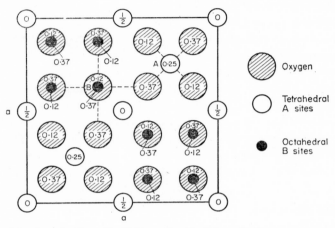

FIG. 6.4. A projection of half the unit cell of the spinel structure on to a cube face. The figures indicate the distances of the atomic centres above the plane of the projection. Metal atoms such as A which occupy the "tetrahedral A sites" are co-ordinated by four oxygen atoms as shown. The atom B on an "octahedral B site" is co-ordinated by six oxygen atoms: four of these are at the level 0·37, one is below (at 0·12) and the other is at an equal distance above in the other half of the cell and accordingly does not appear in the diagram.

the oxygen parameter u from the ideal value of 3/8. There are two possible extremes for the distribution of the metal ions among the two types of site. In what is called the "normal" spinel structure the eight X^{2+} ions occupy the A sites and the sixteen Y^{3+} ions occupy the B sites. In the "inverse" spinel eight of the Y^{3+} ions occupy the A sites and the remaining eight Y^{3+} ions and the eight X^{2+} ions are distributed at random among the B sites. These are two extremes in a continuous distribution of possible cationic arrangements. For a spinel such as $MgFe_2O_4$, in which the metal atoms are very different in atomic number, it is possible to find out whether the structure is "normal" or "inverse" from X-ray diffraction measurements: in fact, this particular ferrite is found[10, 11] to be about 90 per cent inverse. On the other hand, for the mineral spinel itself, $MgAl_2O_4$, and for ferrites such as $MnFe_2O_4$, $ZnFe_2O_4$ it is not very easy to make the distinction with X-rays but it can be readily done with neutrons. Thus for $MgAl_2O_4$, where the scattering lengths of Mg and Al are 0·54, 0·35 $\times$ 10^{-12} cm respectively it can be shown[9] by calculation that the absolute intensity of the (111) reflection would be four times greater for an "inverse" structure than for a "normal" structure. The measured value of this intensity is in favour of an almost completely "normal" structure. $ZnFe_2O_4$ was also found[12] to be completely "normal" but in $MnFe_2O_4$ the arrangement was noticeably less perfect and it was concluded[13] that only 80 per cent of the A sites were occupied by Mn^{2+} ions.

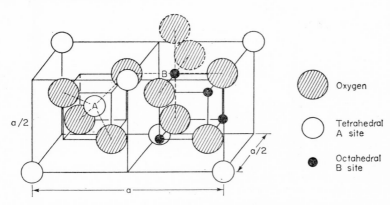

Oxygen

Tetrahedral
A site

Octahedral
B site

FIG. 6.5. A drawing of a quarter of the unit cell of the spinel structure, indicating the occupation of A and B sites by metal ions. A is a typical A-site atom co-ordinated tetrahedrally by the four oxygen atoms shown linked to it by dotted lines. B is a typical B-site atom co-ordinated by the six oxygen atoms shown (the two of these which are shown dotted are situated in neighbouring quarters of the unit cell).

In these structures the relatively large scattering amplitude of oxygen for neutrons, equal to 0·58 $\times$ 10^{-12} cm, means that the oxygen parameter u can be determined very accurately. The most precise way of doing this has been developed by Hastings and Corliss[13] and is illustrated in Fig. 6.6, which illustrates the application of the method to manganese ferrite. The method takes account of both the variation of u and of the parameter x which describes the degree of "normality" of the spinel structure. The procedure is first to calculate the ratio of various pairs or groups of neutron reflections as a function of x, for various values of the oxygen parameter u. The observed experimental value of each ratio is then used to construct a relation between x and u

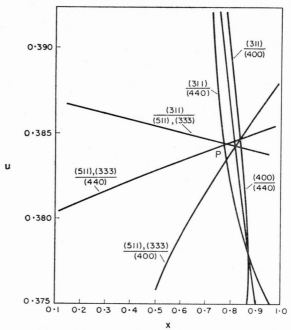

FIG. 6.6. The determination of the oxygen parameter u and the degree of normality x for manganese ferrite $MnFe_2O_4$. From the experimental values of the intensity ratios of various groups of reflections a relation between u and x is deduced. The point of near-intersection of the resulting curves then specifies u and x. (Hastings and Corliss, *Phys. Rev.* 1956, **104**, 328.)

for each set of reflections. A resulting set of curves for $MnFe_2O_4$ is shown in Fig. 6.6 from which it is deduced, by noting the near-intersection of all the curves at the point P, that $u = 0.3846 \pm 0.0003$ and $x = 0.81 \pm 0.03$, corresponding to a predominantly "normal" structure.

REFERENCES

1. MENEGHETTI, D. and SIDHU, S. S.   *Phys. Rev.* 1957, **105**, 130.
2. BACON, G. E.   DUNMUR, I. W., SMITH, J. H. and STREET, R.   *Proc. roy. Soc.* 1957, **241A**, 223.
3. SHULL, C. G. and SIEGEL, S.   *Phys. Rev.* 1949, **75**, 1008.
4. BERGMAN, G. and SHOEMAKER, D. P.   *Acta cryst.* 1954, **7**, 857.
5. DICKINS, G. J., DOUGLAS, A. M. B. and TAYLOR, W. H.   *Acta cryst.* 1956, **9**, 297.
6. *International Tables for X-ray Crystallography* vol. 1.   Kynoch Press, Birmingham, 1952.
7. KASPER, J. S. and WATERSTRAT, R. M.   *Acta cryst.* 1956, **9**, 289.
8. BYKOV, V. N. *et al.* in the press.
9. BACON, G. E.   *Acta cryst.* 1952, **5**, 684.
10. CORLISS, L. M., HASTINGS, J. M. and BROCKMAN, F. G.   *Phys Rev.* 1953, **90**, 1013.
11. BACON, G. E. and ROBERTS, F. F.   *Acta cryst.* 1953, **6**, 57.
12. HASTINGS, J. M. and CORLISS, L. M.   *Rev. mod. Phys.* 1953, **25**, 114.
13. HASTINGS, J. M. and CORLISS, L. M.   *Phys. Rev.* 1956, **104**, 328.

CHAPTER 7

MAGNETIC MATERIALS: AN OUTLINE

ALTHOUGH the magnetic properties of materials are not primarily of chemical interest, a brief outline of the very important contribution of neutron diffraction methods to their study is given here for completeness. This work has depended quite fundamentally on the growth of chemical methods for preparing and extracting many of these substances, particularly the rare-earth compounds and ferrites, in a state of extremely high purity.

7.1. Simple Antiferromagnetic Structures

Some of the earliest observations[1, 2] of neutron diffraction patterns were made with the transition element oxides MnO, FeO, CoO and NiO. These were shown, in due course, to have, below a certain temperature, the magnetic structures of the type shown in Fig. 7.1. It will be noticed immediately that these substances will have no resultant magnetic moment, since as many of the atomic moments point to the left as to the right in the figure, and they are said to be "antiferromagnetic". The magnetic unit cell has, in this case, each of its dimensions twice as large as the chemical cell and because there is additional scattering of the neutron by the magnetic spins this leads to the production of additional reflections in the neutron diffraction pattern. These new reflections can be seen in Fig. 7.2 which compares the pattern of MnO at room temperature, where the thermal motion is too great to permit the establishment of the magnetic order, with the pattern at liquid nitrogen temperature where the order is almost perfectly established. It is from a detailed analysis of these patterns that the magnetic structure of Fig. 7.1 is deduced: the details of the structure cannot be obtained by any other experimental technique, although the onset of magnetic ordering at the so-called Néel temperature may be indicated by rapid changes in certain physical properties such as the magnetic susceptibility and specific heat.

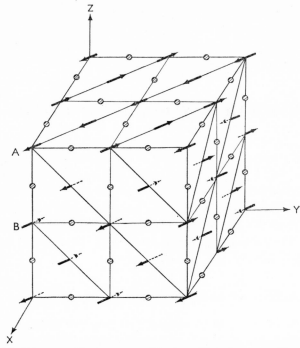

FIG. 7.1. The magnetic structures of the transition-element oxides, such as MnO, indicating the doubled unit-cell when the magnetic moment directions are taken into account. The arrows drawn at the positions of the metal ions indicate the directions of their magnetic moments: the small circles show the intervening oxygen atoms. In each case there are ferromagnetic sheets of atoms parallel to the (111) plane. For MnO, NiO the moments lie in this plane, as shown in the figure, but for FeO they point at right angles to the plane.

Although antiferromagnetism was first studied with neutrons for the transition-element oxides and then for ferrites, such as $MgFe_2O_4$,[3, 4] it is also found to occur in elements, such as chromium[5-9] and manganese,[10] and in many alloys. As examples, the magnetic structure of chromium (in the simple form which is correct to a first approximation) and of MnAu[11] are illustrated in Fig. 7.3. In studying such structures by neutron diffraction the main aim is to discover the particular form of magnetic coupling between the magnetic atoms and to learn how this is related to, and indeed how it reveals to us, the electronic structures of these atoms. For the metals the coupling must be of a direct kind, between one metal atom and its neighbour, but in the case of the oxides shown in Fig. 7.1 for example, where the antiferromagnetic relation is between next-nearest neighbours such as A and B, the coupling between

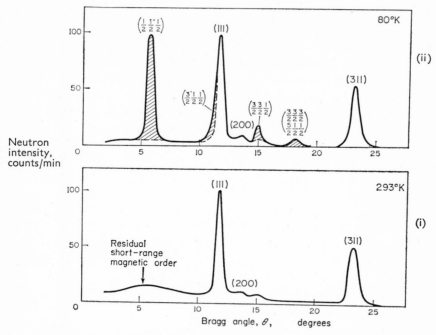

FIG. 7.2. A comparison of the powder diffraction patterns of MnO at (i) 20°C and (ii) −193°C, indicating the additional magnetic reflections which appear at low temperature. Because of the doubled unit cell the magnetic reflections have half-integer indices. (Shull, Strauser and Wollan, *Phys. Rev.* 1951, **83**, 333.)

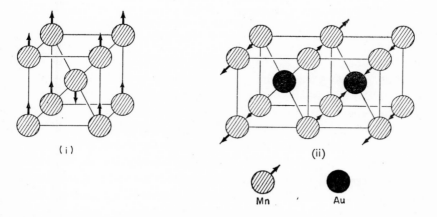

FIG. 7.3. The magnetic unit cells of (i) chromium and (ii) gold–manganese, AuMn, indicating the antiferromagnetic arrangement of the magnetic moments in the structures. In case (ii) the length of the magnetic unit cell is twice as great as the ordinary "chemical" cell in one direction.

the cations must be indirect and must occur via the intervening oxygen atoms. This mechanism is known as "superexchange" and many studies of series of antiferromagnetic compounds—mainly at the Oak Ridge and Brookhaven National Laboratories in the U.S.A.—have been made in order to try and elucidate it. The choice of compounds studied has been made with this aim in view. In particular, the trifluorides[12] and perovskites[13, 14] of the transition elements have been chosen because of their simple structures, which are shown in Fig. 7.4.

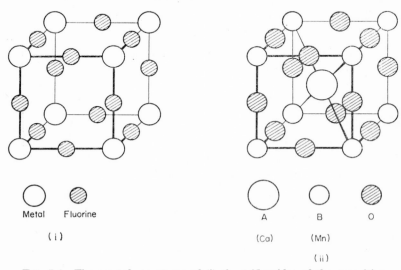

FIG. 7.4. The crystal structures of (i) the trifluorides of the transition metals such as CrF_3, FeF_3 (neglecting a small distortion) and of (ii) the perovskites such as $CaMnO_3$.

In the trifluorides such as CrF_3, FeF_3 the metal atoms lie at the corners of a cube, or a slightly distorted cube, with the intervening fluorine ions placed at the mid-points of the edges. The structure of the perovskites is similar except that there is an additional atom at the body-centre of the cube. In the simplest perovskites for our purpose, such as $CaMnO_3$, the body-centring atom is non-magnetic but, as a further stage in the general study, perovskites containing rare-earth ions as well as the transition metal ions have been examined.[15] In both the trifluorides and the simple perovskites the magnetic coupling between neighbouring cations is via the fluorine or oxygen anion which is midway between them. Two simple magnetic structures have been found and these are illustrated in Fig. 7.5. In the first, (i), all six of the nearest neighbours of a metal ion, have their magnetic moments oppositely directed to it:

in the second type, (ii), only two of the neighbours are coupled anti-ferromagnetically and the remaining four are aligned ferromagnetically. The first type of structure has also been found[16] for most of the double-fluorides, such as $KFeF_3$ and $KNiF_3$, which the divalent transition-group ions form in asociation with potassium.

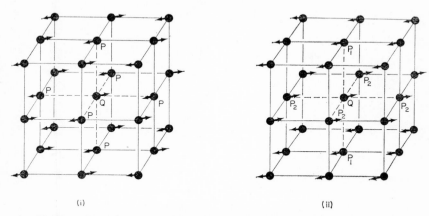

(i)   (ii)

FIG. 7.5. The two principal magnetic structures which have been found in the trifluorides and perovskites of the iron-group metals. Only the magnetic atoms, which are located at the corners of the unit cells, are shown.
In structure (i) all six nearest neighbours P of a typical atom Q have their magnetic moments oppositely directed to that of Q. In (ii) two of the nearest neighbours, P_1, have oppositely-directed moments but the remaining four, P_2, have their moments pointing in the same direction as the moment at Q.

In another comprehensive series of studies the three polymorphic forms of manganese sulphide, MnS, have been examined,[17] and the different magnetic structures of MnS, MnSe and MnTe have been compared.[18] The different arrangements of nearest neighbours in the rock salt, zinc blende, and wurtzite structures of the sulphides are contrasted in Fig. 7.6. These results have been discussed theoretically by Danielian and Stevens.[19]

7.2. Rare-earth Nitrides

Quite a different kind of magnetic behaviour has been found[20] in the rare-earth nitrides, such as HoN and TbN, which have the same crystallographic structure (the NaCl type) as the $3d$-transition metal oxides, represented by MnO. HoN and TbN become ferromagnetic when cooled below temperatures of 18°K and 43°K respectively, and

9

above these temperatures their diffraction patterns simply show nuclear reflections superimposed on an intense background due to paramagnetic scattering. The magnitude of this background is what would be expected for the free ions, namely for a magnetic moment of $10\cdot6\mu_B$

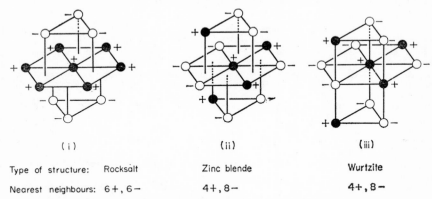

(i)	(ii)	(iii)

Type of structure:	Rocksalt	Zinc blende	Wurtzite
Nearest neighbours:	6+, 6−	4+, 8−	4+, 8−

FIG. 7.6. A comparison of the different arrangement of magnetic moments on nearest-neighbour metal ions for the three polymorphic forms of MnS. In the rock-salt and zinc-blende type structures there is cubic close-packing of the metal atoms (with different arrangements of the S atoms): in the wurtzite modification the manganese atoms are in hexagonal close-packing. (Corliss, Elliott and Hastings, *Phys. Rev.* 1956, **104**, 924.)

for Ho^{3+} and $9\cdot0\mu_B$ for Tb^{3+}. The pattern for HoN at room temperature is shown as the upper curve in Fig. 7.7 and is interesting because the only nuclear reflections which appear are those for which all the indices are even. The reflections with all odd indices are missing because the nuclear scattering amplitudes of holmium and nitrogen are practically equal. Below their Curie temperatures these nitrides become ferromagnetic, with disappearance of the paramagnetic background scattering and the production of coherent magnetic reflections. Since the magnetic arrangement is ferromagnetic there is no doubling of the unit cell size and the magnetic reflections show simply as increased intensities at the angular positions of the nuclear reflections, appearing of course whether the indices are odd or even. The lower curve of Fig. 7.7 shows the intensity difference pattern between room temperature and $1\cdot3°K$, which is far below the Curie temperature, for HoN. The surprising feature is that the magnitude of the magnetic reflections is less than expected. The apparent moments for Ho^{3+}, Tb^{3+} are certainly not greater than 8·6 and $7\cdot0\mu_B$ respectively and these values are significantly lower than the paramagnetic values mentioned previously. This be-

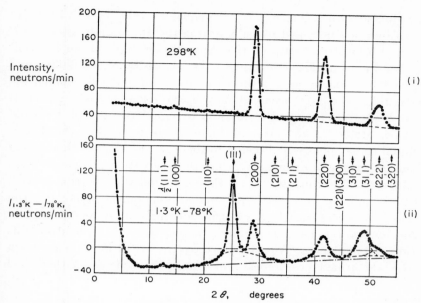

Fig. 7.7. The powder diffraction pattern of HoN at room temperature is shown at curve (i). The crystal structure is of the NaCl type but reflections with all indices odd are missing because the nuclear scattering amplitudes of Ho, N are practically equal. Curve (ii) shows the *difference* in intensity between patterns at 1·3°K and at 78°K, representing *ferromagnetic* scattering for all the reflections allowed by the face-centred cubic symmetry, whether the indices be all odd or all even. (Wilkinson *et al. J. Appl. Phys.* 1960, **31,** 358 S.)

haviour has been interpreted by Trammell in terms of changes in the energy levels of these ions because of the crystalline field interactions.

7.3. Ferrimagnetic Structures of Ferrites

We have already mentioned the structures of the ferrites in Chapter 6, where we were interested in the ability of neutrons to distinguish between atoms of neighbouring atomic number. In the present discussion we are more concerned with the ability of neutrons to determine the direction and magnitude of the magnetic moments on the cations in the spinel structure. This was achieved first[21] for the simplest ferrite, magnetite Fe_3O_4, and was one of the most spectacular successes of neutron diffraction and a complete justification of Néel's hypotheses. Unlike X-rays, neutrons are able to distinguish between the ions Fe^{2+}, Fe^{3+}, since these have different spin quantum numbers of 2 and 5/2 respectively and the corresponding magnetic scattering amplitudes in the forward direction, $\theta = 0°$, are equal to $1{\cdot}09$, $1{\cdot}36 \times 10^{-12}$ cm. These values are obtained by substituting the appropriate values of S in eqn. (1.5.1). By separating the magnetic scattering from the contribution due to nuclear scattering it was shown by Shull, Wollan and Koehler[21] that magnetite has the structure of an "inverse" spinel: the tetrahedral A sites are occupied only by Fe^{3+} ions whereas the octahedral B sites are occupied at random by equal number of Fe^{2+} and Fe^{3+} ions. Moreover, the magnetic moments of the ions on the A sites are found to be oppositely directed to those on the B sites, thus giving a resultant magnetic moment which is the equivalent of one Fe^{2+} ion per "molecule". Thus we have the characteristic "ferrimagnetic" structure, halfway between ferro- and antiferro-magnetism, and the details of this structure, which was originally inferred by Néel to explain the magnetization data, are entirely supported by the neutron diffraction measurements. A portion of the structure of Fe_3O_4 is shown in Fig. 7.8: the atomic positions are, of course, the same as for the spinel

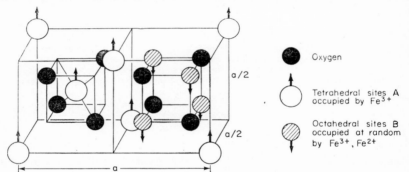

FIG. 7.8. The "inverse" spinel structure of magnetite, showing a quarter of the unit cell. All the tetrahedral A-sites are occupied by Fe^{3+} ions with their moments directed upwards. The octahedral B sites are filled at random by the remainder of the Fe^{3+} ions and all the Fe^{2+} ions: all the magnetic moments of B-site ions are directed downwards.

structure which we showed in Fig. 6.5. We are now able to specify the allocation of the Fe^{2+} and Fe^{3+} ions among the tetrahedral and octahedral sites, and to show the directions of their magnetic moments.

We have seen earlier that in a magnetic material the effective scattering amplitude is proportional to $\sin \beta$, where β is the angle between the moment direction and the scattering vector which we showed in Fig. 1.3. In a ferromagnetic or ferrimagnetic material we can control the direction of the magnetic moments by applying a magnetic field. If the field is applied along the scattering vector then β is zero and the magnetic

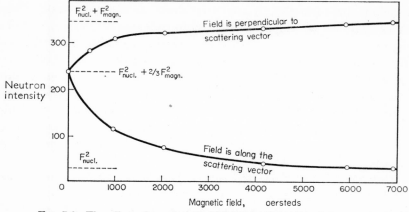

FIG. 7.9. The effect of a magnetic field on the intensity of the (111) reflection from magnetite, Fe_3O_4. When the field is applied along the scattering vector the magnetic component of the intensity falls to zero. If the field is applied perpendicular to the scattering vector the magnetic contribution rises to a maximum, at which the magnetic scattering amplitude p is fully effective. (Shull, Wollan and Koehler, *Phys. Rev.* 1951, **84**, 912.)

scattering disappears: on the other hand, if the field is at right angles to the scattering vector, then $\sin \beta$ becomes unity and the magnetic scattering is increased to a maximum. An experimental demonstration[21] of this dependence of the magnetic scattering on the magnitude and direction of an applied field is illustrated in Fig. 7.9 for the (111) reflection of magnetite. In practice this behaviour provides a means of deciding what portion of the resultant neutron scattering at any angular position is magnetic in origin. This method was used to find separately the nuclear and magnetic scattering contributions in the study of magnetite which we have just been discussing. The method can only be applied to substances which have a resultant magnetization, i.e. to ferro- and ferri-magnetic materials, and cannot be used with antiferromagnetic materials, since in these latter the magnetic moments are not usually rotated by applied fields. However, in antiferromagnetic substances the magnetic scattering can be distinguished by its temperature-dependence and often by the fact that new reflections appear which are not observed in an X-ray diffraction pattern and which are due to a doubling of the unit cell in one or more directions.

7.4. More Complicated Magnetic Structures

Even these relatively simple magnetic structures are far from completely understood and it is not surprising that in the course of this work more complicated structures have been found in which many challenging problems of interpretation appear. Certain compounds, such as $MnBr_2$, $MnCl_2$, exhibit a mixture of properties partly characteristic of ferromagnetism and partly of antiferromagnetism and they are sensitive to the application of external magnetic fields. $MnBr_2$ has a hexagonal structure[22] in which layers of manganese atoms are separated by pairs of layers of halogen atoms. Each layer of metal atoms forms a ferromagnetic sheet and neighbouring layers are normally coupled antiferromagnetically but the latter coupling can be broken down by applying an external magnetic field.

Another very interesting structure is shown by $MnAu_2$ where the magnetic manganese atoms again lie in layers but instead of there being a simple $+ - + -$ change in moment direction from layer to layer we now find[23] a continuous rotation of the moment direction, which produces the spiral structure shown in Fig. 7.10. There is a rotation of about $52°$ between the moment directions in successive sheets, so that the

FIG. 7.10. The spiral arrangement of magnetic moments in $MnAu_2$. The structure is built up of ferromagnetic sheets of manganese atoms and there is a rotation of $52°$, about the z-axis, between the directions of the magnetic moments in successive sheets, giving a repeating unit of seven sheets.

c-dimension of the magnetic unit cell is about $3\frac{1}{2}$ times as large as that of the ordinary chemical cell. A similar type of spiral arrangement of spins is found in MnO_2 and for some of the rare-earth metals. An even longer range magnetic periodicity superimposed on the crystallographic unit cell is displayed by the metal chromium. The simple antiferromagnetic structure which we showed in Fig. 7.3 (i) is only a first approximation to the truth. Intensive studies[6, 7, 8, 9] of the diffraction pattern, particularly using single crystals, have revealed the presence of satellite reflections which can only be accounted for by the existence of a second periodicity of about 28 unit cells. This can be interpreted in several different ways. First, there may be a succession of "antiphase domains" which are produced by a regular occurrence of an error in the $+ - + -$ sequence of magnetic moments for the corner and body-centre atoms. Alternatively, there may be a spiral arrangement of moments, as is found in $MnAu_2$, with a rotation of about $13°$ between the moments in successive unit cells, thus again leading to an overall superimposed period of 28 unit cells. A third possibility is that the actual value of the aligned component of magnetic moment varies sinusoidally over the blocks of unit cells. In fact, this more complicated model is attractive because it allows the simplest interpretation of a change at low temperature, near $150°K$, where the moment directions appear to flip over through $90°$. In principle a distinction can be made between these different models by a careful study of the details of the satellite reflections in the diffraction pattern: however, the final solution to this problem is still uncertain.

The spiral arrangement of magnetic spins which we have just discussed is an example of a non-collinear arrangement, in contrast to the simple antiferromagnetic structure in which the spins all lie parallel to a single direction, though they may be oriented either positively or negatively with respect to it. A second kind of non-collinear arrangement has been found in chromium selenide, $CrSe$, in which the spins are arranged in an umbrella fashion as shown in Fig. 7.11. The axis of the umbrella is oppositely directed in the successive layers of chromium atoms. Because the magnetic moments are inclined with respect to the z-axis it follows that the effective antiferromagnetic moment is reduced and it is concluded from the intensities of the magnetic reflections that it is equal to $2·9\mu_B$ per chromium atom. If the orbital moment is completely quenched it would be expected that the actual magnetic moment of a Cr^{2+} ion would be equal to $4\mu_B$. It is concluded therefore that the spins are inclined to the z-axis at an angle of approximately $45°$.

Even more complicated arrangements of magnetic spins, giving both ferromagnetic and antiferromagnetic properties, have been observed in the rare-earth metals. Particularly the later elements in the series— terbium, dysprosium, holmium, erbium and thulium—have been studied[25, 26] in single-crystal form at Oak Ridge. Unlike the preceding members of the series (samarium, europium and gadolinium) these later elements have fairly low neutron absorption coefficients and this, together with the very large magnetic moments of the rare-earth ions,

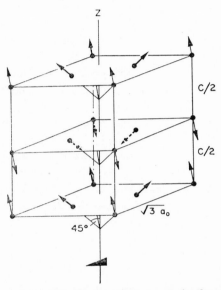

Fig. 7.11. The arrangement of magnetic moments in chromium selenide. The magnetic unit cell has an a dimension which is $\sqrt{3}$ times as large as the dimension a_0 of the ordinary chemical cell. The magnetic spins are inclined at about 45° to the z-axis and are arranged in umbrella fashion about a triad axis: they are oppositely directed in successive sheets. (After Corliss, et al. Phys Rev. 1961, **122**, 1402.)

has simplified their study. The metals have the simple hexagonal close-packed crystal structure and when cooled they are, in general, found to order antiferromagnetically: then, at lower temperatures, they become ferromagnetic. Basically the antiferromagnetic structures are of two types. In terbium, dysprosium and holmium there is a spiral arrangement of magnetic spins such as we described for MnAu₂. The axis of the spiral is along the c crystallographic axis and the magnetic moments are perpendicular to this. For erbium and thulium, however, the moments are directed along the c axis and the magnitude of the effective moment varies sinusoidally along this axis. In some cases these descriptions are certainly only first approximations to the precise magnetic structures and in erbium, for example, it is found that there is a transition at an intermediate temperature from the sinusoidal-modulation type of structure to the spin-spiral model. These fascinating studies are still continuing and the reader who is interested is referred to the latest papers[25, 26] in the literature.

REFERENCES

1. SHULL, C. G. and SMART, J. S. *Phys. Rev.* 1949, **76**, 1256.
2. SHULL, C. G., STRAUSER, W. A. and WOLLAN, E. O. *Phys. Rev.* 1951, **83**, 333.
3. CORLISS, L. M., HASTINGS, J. M. and BROCKMAN, F. G. *Phys. Rev.* 1953, **90**, 1013.
4. BACON, G. E. and ROBERTS, F. F. *Acta cryst.* 1953, **6**, 57.
5. SHULL, C. G. and WILKINSON, M. K. *Rev. mod. Phys.* 1953, **25**, 100.
6. CORLISS, L. M., HASTINGS, J. M. and WEISS, R. J. *Phys. Rev. Letters*, 1959, **3**, 211.
7. BACON, G. E. *Acta cryst.* 1961, **14**, 823.
8. SHIRANE, G. and TAKEI, W. J. *J. Phys. Soc. Japan*, 1962, **17**, Suppl. B-III, 35.
9. BYKOV, V. N. *et al. Doklady Akad. Nauk.* SSSR. 1959, **128**, 1153.
10. KASPER, J. S. and ROBERTS, B. W. *Phys. Rev.* 1956, **101**, 537.
11. BACON, G. E. and STREET, R. S. *Proc. phys. Soc. Lond.* 1958, **72**, 470.
    BACON, G. E. *Proc. phys. Soc. Lond.* 1962.
12. WOLLAN, E. O., CHILD, H. R., KOEHLER, W. C. and WILKINSON, M. K. *Phys. Rev.* 1958, **112**, 1132.
13. WOLLAN, E. O. and KOEHLER, W. C. *Phys. Rev.* 1955, **100**, 545.
14. KOEHLER, W. C. and WOLLAN, E. O. *J. Phys. Chem. Solids*, 1957, **2**, 100.
15. KOEHLER, W. C., WOLLAN, E. O. and WILKINSON, M. K. *Phys. Rev.* 1960, **118**, 58.
16. SCATTURIN, V., CORLISS, L. M., ELLIOTT, N. and HASTINGS, J. M. *Acta cryst.* 1961, **14**, 19.
17. CORLISS, L. M., ELLIOTT, N. and HASTINGS, J. M. *Phys. Rev.* 1956, **104**, 924.
18. HASTINGS, J. M., ELLIOTT, N. and CORLISS, L. M. *Phys. Rev.* 1959, **115**, 13.
19. DANIELIAN, A. and STEVENS, K. W. H. *Proc. phys. Soc. Lond.* 1961, **77**, 124.
20. WILKINSON, M. K. *et al. J. Appl. Phys.* 1960, **31**, 358 S.
21. SHULL, C. G., WOLLAN, E. O. and KOEHLER, W. C. *Phys. Rev.* 1951, **84**, 912.
22. WOLLAN, E. O., KOEHLER, W. C. and WILKINSON, M. K. *Phys. Rev.* 1958, **110**, 638.
23. HERPIN, A., MERIEL, P. and VILLAIN, J. *C.R. Acad. Sci. Paris* 1959, **249**, 1334.
24. CORLISS, L. M. *et al. Phys. Rev.* 1961, **122**, 1402.
25. WILKINSON, M. K. *et al. J. Phys. Soc. Japan*, 1962, **17**, Suppl. B-III, 27.
26. KOEHLER, W. C. *et al. J. Phys. Soc. Japan*, 1962, **17**, Suppl. B-III, 32.

CHAPTER 8

THE STUDY OF LIQUIDS AND GASES

8.1. Introduction

When a solid melts to form a liquid the 3-dimensional order is destroyed but there still remains a good deal of structural regularity which can be studied by diffraction methods. Even in a gas it is possible to determine the interatomic separations within molecules by observing the angular distribution of the scattered radiation. In principle, the study of liquids and gases by neutron diffraction follows the same procedures as when X-rays are used. The angular distribution of the scattered neutrons is measured and then converted into an atomic distribution curve by a Fourier transformation. The intensity $I(2\theta)$ at a scattering angle 2θ is usually expressed as $I(s)$, where the variable s is equal to $(4\pi \sin \theta)/\lambda$, and the atomic density $\rho(r)$ at a distance r from an average atom is then given by

$$4\pi r^2[\rho(r) - \rho_0] = \frac{2r}{\pi} \int_0^\infty s \, \frac{I(s) - I(\infty)}{I(\infty)} \sin rs \, ds$$

where $I(\infty)$ is the value of $I(s)$ as $s \to \infty$, and ρ_0 is the mean atomic density of the liquid. Compared with X-ray scattering, neutron diffraction offers the advantage that the atoms are point scatterers—since it is the nucleus which gives rise to the scattering—and therefore the magnitude of the scattering by an individual atom does not fall off as the angle of scattering increases. Uncertainties due to imprecise knowledge of atomic scattering curves are therefore avoided. On the other hand the reduction of coherent scattering because of the thermal motion of the atoms is the same for neutrons as for X-rays and this will smear out much of the detail which would otherwise be gained from the high-angle portions of the diffraction patterns.

From a practical point of view the low absorption coefficients of most materials for neutrons mean that it is much easier to devise suitable containers for holding liquids and gases, and it is quite simple to study them over a wide range of temperature and pressure. Moreover, the

122

fact that the low coefficients of absorption for neutrons permit the use of much larger samples than in X-ray diffraction means that any contamination of the liquid surface is much less important.

8.2. Experimental Studies of Liquids

The first neutron-diffraction studies of liquids were made in 1950 by Chamberlain[1] who examined liquid samples of sulphur, lead and bismuth. However, only a relatively low neutron intensity was available at this time and the use of a rather wide spread of wavelength, which was necessary in order to increase the intensity, added to the inaccuracies in interpreting the data.

Some subsequent studies have been made on liquid lead and bismuth but the results have not been entirely consistent, thus emphasizing the difficulties in this kind of work which limit the accuracy with which the atomic distribution in the liquid can be deduced from the diffraction pattern. There are many factors for which corrections have to be applied, such as incoherent scattering, inelastic scattering, multiple scattering and the fact that the experimental measurements of intensity can only be carried out up to some limited value of $(\sin \theta)/\lambda$. The most recent studies[2] of lead and bismuth were made as part of an extended series of observations by both X-rays and neutrons with a range of alloys as well as the two pure metals. A series of neutron patterns from this work is illustrated in Fig. 8.1 and the corresponding atomic density functions are shown in Fig. 8.2. The differences in the latter are more pronounced than in the diffraction patterns themselves, and lead to the conclusion that the number of nearest-neighbours is close to 12 in liquid lead, and retains this value in alloys which contain up to about 60 per cent of bismuth. The number then falls to about 7·7 in pure bismuth. The nearest-neighbour distance varies from 3·40 Å in pure lead to 3·36 Å in bismuth and the conclusions drawn from the X-ray and neutron patterns are in good agreement.

An earlier study of mercury by Vineyard[3] emphasizes an advantage of neutrons in permitting the use of a simple transmission technique, in contrast to the X-ray measurements which were made by reflection from the liquid surface and which gave varying results in different circumstances. In the atomic distribution which was deduced from the neutron-diffraction pattern, there were found to be 8·3 nearest neighbours at a separation of about 3·1 Å. There was no evidence of an inner peak which had been reported in some of the X-ray patterns.

Some very detailed work on liquid oxygen and nitrogen has been carried out by Henshaw, Hurst and Pope,[4] taking advantage of the high neutron intensity which was available at the Chalk River reactor. The radial distribution functions obtained in the two cases are shown in Fig. 8.3. For nitrogen the first peak is at a radius of 1.1 Å and the number of atoms under this peak is equal to 1·0. This atom therefore forms a close pair with the postulated atom at the origin, thus providing direct evidence that nitrogen is diatomic in the liquid state, with an interatomic separation of 1·1 Å. The second peak is found at a radius of 4·4 Å and corresponds to the presence of 23·6 atoms or 11·8 diatomic molecolues, practically equal to the number of 12 which would give an arrangement of close-packing. For oxygen, however, the first peak at a

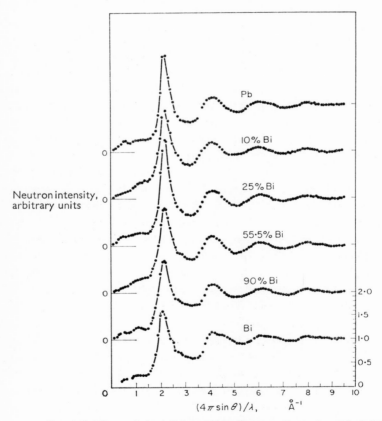

Fig. 8.1. The variation of the scattered neutron intensity with $4\pi(\sin\theta)/\lambda$ for liquid lead and bismuth and for several liquid alloys with the compositions in weight percent as indicated: the angle of scattering is equal to 2θ.
(Sharrah, Petz and Kruh, *J. chem. Phys.* 1960, **32**, 241.)

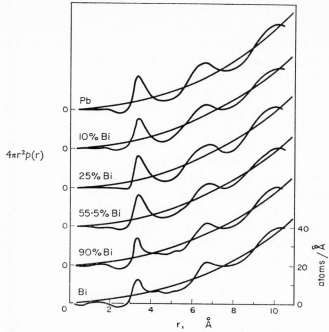

FIG. 8.2. The radial distribution function of atomic density $4\pi r^2 \rho(r)$ for liquid lead and bismuth and intermediate alloys. The parabolic curves are those for which would be obtained for a "structureless" liquid of uniform density. (Sharrah, Petz and Kruh, *J. chem. Phys.* 1960, **32**, 241.)

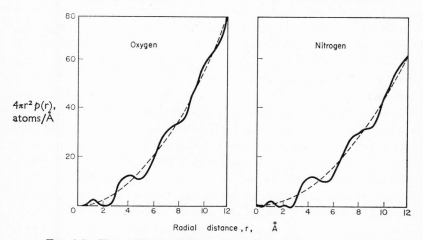

FIG. 8.3. The radial distribution curves $4\pi r^2 \rho(r)$ for liquid oxygen and nitrogen, together with the smooth curve of $4\pi r^2 \rho_0$ which is the corresponding function for uniform density. (Henshaw, Hurst and Pope, *Phys. Rev.* 1953, **92**, 1229.)

radius of 1·25 Å corresponds to 1·5 atoms, thus suggesting that the molecular grouping in the liquid state consists, on the average, of 2·5 atoms. This is consistent with the results of spectroscopic and magnetic measurements which suggest the existence of some O_4 groups.

Gingrich and Heaton[5] have made measurements of the scattering from the liquid alkali-metals lithium, sodium, potassium, rubidium and cesium. X-rays had previously been used to examine the first three of these, but not the last two, which are difficult to study with X-rays because of their high absorption coefficients. These measurements provide a good example of the ease with which such samples can be contained and heated for study with neutrons. The liquids were contained in vanadium cylinders about 1 cm in diameter and with a wall-thickness of 0·01 cm, sealed with vanadium ends under an atmosphere of argon. The advantage of using vanadium for the containers is that its coherent scattering amplitude is practically zero. The results for the light atom lithium, in the form of the isotope Li^7 to reduce absorption, are particularly interesting because they show that these atoms behave as if they were free in the liquid state. At large angles of scattering we would expect the intensity of neutron scattering to reach a constant value, since interference effects from different atoms will have become insignificant and there should be no fall-off of atomic scattering factor with angle as occurs for X-rays. Indeed, the experimental patterns which we showed earlier for lead and bismuth in Fig. 8.1 show very clearly this expected constancy in the magnitude of the scattering at high angles. In the case of lithium, however, the intensity falls off markedly with increasing angle, as illustrated in Fig. 8.4. If it is assumed that the lithium atoms are free and that they recoil from the incident neutrons then this fall-off of intensity is expected and correction for this effect leads to the essentially horizontal curve which is also shown in Fig. 8.4. A small depression is found for sodium for the same reason but the effect is negligible for potassium and the heavier alkali metals: a very marked effect of the same kind has been reported in the scattering of neutrons by liquid helium. Figure 8.5 shows the atomic distributions which were deduced for the various alkali metals just above their melting points. The curves are all very similar in general features and show a steady increase of the nearest-neighbour distance from 3·15 Å in lithium to 5·31 Å in cesium. For all the five metals the number of nearest-neighbours was found to lie between 9 and 9·5. Observations with rubidium and cesium at temperatures up to a few hundred degrees above their melting points showed the progressive growth of a sub-

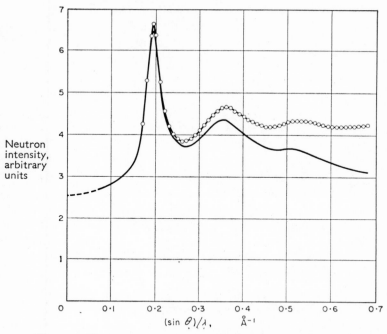

Neutron intensity, arbitrary units

$(\sin \theta)/\lambda$, $\overset{\circ}{A}^{-1}$

FIG. 8.4. The neutron scattering pattern of liquid lithium at 180°C is indicated by the lower line, with the intensity falling off at high angles. The upper line shows a constant intensity at high angles when correction is made for recoil of the free lithium atoms. (Gingrich and Heaton, *J. chem. Phys.* 1961, **34**, 873.)

sidiary peak between the first and second peaks in the distribution curves, but no such effect was noticed for the lighter elements.

All but one of the studies of liquids which we have so far described have been for elements. The one exception has been the liquid alloys of the heavy metals lead and bismuth. We shall now describe the study by Levy *et al*,[6] of molten salts which contain two atomic species, namely the ions of an alkali metal and a halogen. LiCl, KCl and CsBr were examined by both X-rays and neutrons and several other salts were studied by X-rays alone. In the case of the lithium salt, material consisting entirely of the Li[7] isotope was used in order to reduce the absorption coefficient for neutrons, which is very large for Li[6]. The experimentally measured scattering curves for the molten liquids were converted into pair radial-distribution functions which express the probability that *pairs* of atoms are to be found separated by a given distance. With LiCl, for example, this function will be the superposition of the

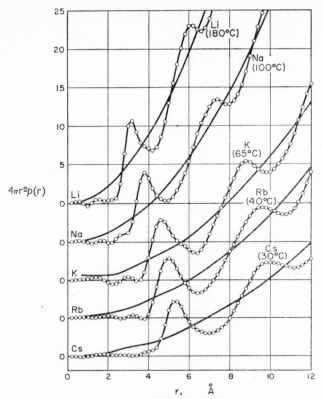

$4\pi r^2 \rho(r)$

Fig. 8.5. The radial distribution functions $4\pi r^2 \rho(r)$ for the liquid alkali metals, measured at temperatures just above their melting-points. (Gingrich and Heaton, *J. chem. Phys.* 1961, **34**, 873.)

separate probability curves for the three pairs of ions Li^+Cl^-, Li^+Li^+ and Cl^-Cl^-. The particular contribution which the use of neutrons made to this study can be realized by considering Fig. 8.6 which shows the pair radial-distribution functions for molten Li^7Cl, KCl and CsBr. The area under any peak in a distribution curve will be proportional not only to the numbers of ion pairs but also to the product of the neutron scattering amplitudes of the two ions which contribute to the peak. It will be seen that for LiCl the first large peak at 2·45 Å is negative. Since the scattering amplitude of Li^7 is negative but that of Cl is positive, this first peak must therefore be due to the Li–Cl interaction and it can then be deduced that the nearest-neighbours of each ion are, approximately, four ions of opposite sign. The X-ray curve for Li^7Cl, is in marked contrast to the neutron result and shows, as expected, a

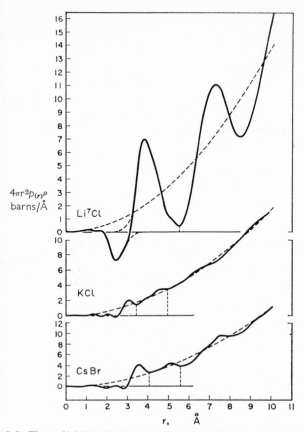

FIG. 8.6. The radial distribution functions for molten samples of Li⁷Cl, KCl and CsBr as determined from the neutron scattering patterns. The first large peak for Li⁷Cl at 2·45 Å is negative, indicating that nearest neighbours are ions of opposite charge, since these have neutron-scattering amplitudes of opposite sign for this particular salt. The peaks for KCl at 3·10 Å and CsBr at 3·55 Å are both positive. (Levy *et al.*, *Ann. N.Y. Acad. Sci.* 1960, **79**, 762.)

first peak which is positive. The first peaks in the neutron distribution functions for KCl and CsBr are positive, at 3·10 and 3·55 Å respectively, and this is again what would be expected since all these four elements have positive scattering amplitudes for neutrons.

8.3. Condensed Inert Gases

Perhaps the most interesting studies of liquids have been for the condensed forms of the inert gases argon, neon, krypton and helium which have been carried out by Henshaw and his co-workers[7, 8, 9] at

Chalk River. These elements are the ones which are most amenable to theoretical calculation, particularly in relation to the solid–liquid transformation.

The results of a typical experiment are shown in Fig. 8.7 which shows a scattering curve for liquid neon, contained in an aluminium cassette at 26°K and a pressure of 1·7 atmospheres, as measured by Henshaw.[9]

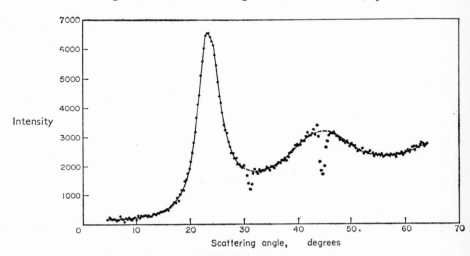

FIG. 8.7. The angular distribution of neutrons as scattered by liquid neon at 26°K and 1·7 atmospheres pressure after correction for background effects, for a neutron wavelength of 1·06 Å. (Henshaw, *Phys. Rev.* 1958, **111**, 1470.)

The two small dotted regions of the curve occur where the scattering due to the liquid cannot be determined accurately because of the relatively intense coherent scattering from the aluminium container. From this curve can be calculated both the radial-distribution function, $4\pi r^2[\rho(r)-\rho_0]$, in atoms per angstrom which is shown in Fig. 8.8, and the atomic distribution function $4\pi r\rho(r)$ atoms per angstrom,[2] shown in Fig. 8.9. From zero up to a distance of about 2·45 Å, which is the nearest distance of approach of two atoms in the liquid, the ordinate in Fig. 8.8 is approximately equal to $4\pi r^2\rho_0$, which is the dotted curve, and the ordinate in Fig. 8.9 is equal to zero. The distribution then rises to a peak at 3·17 Å which represents the most probable distance of approach of two atoms and which is to be compared with a distance of 3·13 Å which occurs in the solid. From the area under this peak it can be calculated that there are about 8·8 atoms in this shell of nearest-neighbours which surrounds any individual atom, in comparison with

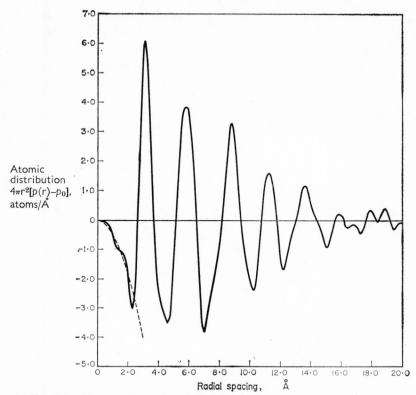

FIG. 8.8. The radial distribution function $4\pi r^2(\rho(r) - \rho_0)$ for liquid neon, as calculated from the scattering pattern shown in Fig. 8.7. At small distances $\rho(r)$ is zero and the function is equal to $-4\pi r^2 \rho_0$, which is indicated by the dotted curve. (Henshaw, *Phys. Rev.* 1958, **111**, 1470.)

the 12 neighbours which are present in the face-centred cubic solid. It seems likely that the basic structure must be different in the two cases and that the change from solid to liquid is neither a simple expansion nor a uniform random removal of atoms. The measured decrease in density is going from solid to liquid is about 10 per cent, but the increase in volume of the first shell of atoms is, from the above values, only about 4 per cent and at the same time the number of neighbours falls from 12 to 8·8, that is by 27 per cent.

A very similar conclusion is reached by Henshaw for the transformation between solid and liquid argon, for which the number of nearest-neighbours are 12 and 8·2 respectively. This amounts to a reduction of 32 per cent during the transformation from solid to liquid whereas the density falls by only 14 per cent. Previously, Hurst and Henshaw[7] studied the scattering of neutrons by liquid helium, in particular to see whether any change in atomic distribution accompanied the change from He I to He II at the lambda-point temperature. No significant change was observed and, in common with liquid neon and argon, there were about 8 nearest neighbours to each atom, at a distance of about 3·6 Å. Observations were made at 5·04, 4·24, 2·25, 2·15, 1·95 and 1·65°K and it was found that the peak in the distribution curve fell from 3·68 Å at 5° to 3·50 Å at about 2°K. The compression indicated

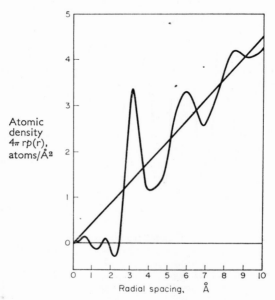

FIG. 8.9. The atomic distribution function $4\pi r\rho(r)$ for liquid neon which shows that the nearest distance of approach of two atoms is 2·45 Å and the most probable distance of separation of nearest neighbours is 3·17 Å, compared with 3·13 Å for the measured spacing between two atoms in the solid at 4·2°K. (Henshaw, *Phys. Rev.* 1958, **111**, 1470.)

by this movement is not consistent with the change of density which occurs and which is significantly greater. It seems therefore that when the temperature of the liquid is increased there is a progressive growth in unoccupied sites, so that the density falls more rapidly than the mere expansion of the nearest-neighbour distance would indicate. The curves of radial density distribution which were deduced at three different temperatures are shown in Fig. 8·10. The position of the peak moves by only about 5 per cent whereas the density change from 0·095 to 0·146 would mean a movement of the peak corresponding to a ratio

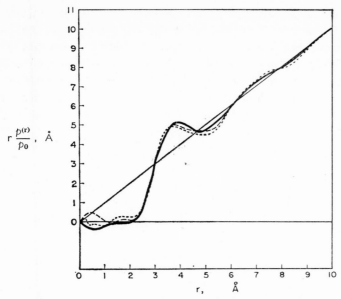

FIG. 8.10. The radial distribution curves for liquid helium at three different temperatures, showing the small change in the position of the most probable distance of separation for nearest-neighbour atoms in the liquid. The ordinate is $r\rho(r)/\rho_0$ where ρ_0 is the mean atomic density. The full line is at 5·04°, the broken line is at 4·24°K and the dotted line is the average value between 1·65°K and 2·25°K. (Hurst and Henshaw, *Phys. Rev.* 1955, **100**, 994.)

$(0·146/0·095)^{1/3}:1$, which is about 15 per cent, if there was a simple dilation of the structure.

8.4. Fused Silica

It is convenient to insert at this point a mention of a study of the neutron scattering by amorphous silica, which was examined at an early date by Milligan, Levy and Peterson.[10] A comparison of their diffraction patterns with the original X-ray pattern published by Warren[11] in 1934 illustrates how additional detail can be secured at high angles when neutrons are used. The two sets of patterns are reproduced in Fig. 8.11.

8.5. Scattering by Gases

In a gas there is no correlation between the positions of neighbouring molecules and, consequently, the detail of the neutron-diffraction pattern will depend on the internuclear distances within the molecule and on the nuclear vibrations. Some measurements have been made by Alcock and Hurst[12, 13, 14] for the gases H_2, D_2, O_2, CO_2, N_2, CF_4 and CH_4. The experiments are very difficult because the scattering by gases at ordinary pressure is so weak. In order to achieve any worthwhile accuracy in the measurements it was necessary to compress the gases to about 30 atmospheres and at this pressure it becomes necessary to make a small correction for an interference effect between neighbouring molecules.

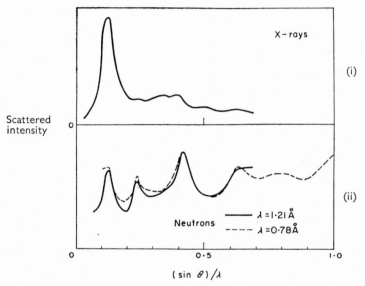

Fig. 8.11. A comparison of (i) X-ray and (ii) neutron scattering patterns for amorphous silica. Two neutron curves are shown, using wavelengths of 0·78 and 1·21 Å respectively. (From Shull and Wollan, *Solid State Physics*, vol. 2, Academic Press, New York, 1956.)

A typical neutron scattering curve is shown at (i) in Fig. 8.12 for oxygen. The peak in the curve at a value of $(\sin \theta)/\lambda$ equal to about 0·5 indicates an interatomic separation in the oxygen molecules of about 1·2 Å. It will be noticed that the peak in the diffraction curve occurs at a much greater value of $(\sin \theta)/\lambda$ than, for example, the first peak in the pattern of liquid lithium which we showed in Fig. 8.4, where we were concerned with the much larger interatomic separation of 3·15 Å. It follows therefore that for *gases* the ability of the neutron pattern to show detail out to large values of $(\sin \theta)/\lambda$, without being smeared out by a falling atomic scattering factor, is particularly important. Indeed, in the corresponding scattering curve for X-rays which is shown as curve (ii) in Fig. 8.12, the peak due to the O—O separation is almost completely obliterated. An example of a more complicated molecule is provided by gaseous CF_4, which yields two peaks in its diffraction pattern. These can be shown to correspond to interatomic separations of 2·17 Å and 1·33 Å which are interpreted in terms of a tetrahedral CF_4 molecule with an edge of 2·17 Å for the F—F distance, and a corner-to-centre distance of 1·33 Å for the C—F bond. It is found that

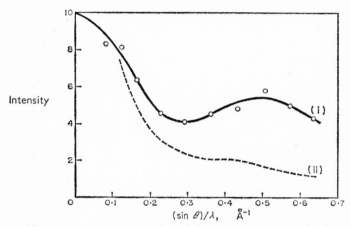

FIG. 8.12. The scattering by diatomic oxygen, showing a comparison of the neutron data of Alcock and Hurst (i) with the X-ray data (ii) of Gajewski. In the former there is a marked peak of intensity which corresponds to an interatomic separation of 1·2 Å but this is barely distinguishable in the X-ray pattern. (From *Neutron Diffraction*, Bacon, Oxford University Press, London.)

there is some decrease in the intensity of the neutron scattering at high angles on account of intra-molecular vibrations and the accuracy of the experimental data is sufficient to estimate magnitudes for these which are in agreement with spectroscopic information.

A complete interpretation of these scattering experiments requires a detailed quantum-mechanical treatment, particularly for heavy molecules, but it was found that a semi-classical approximation gave very reasonable results. This problem is discussed in detail by Pope.[15]

REFERENCES

1. CHAMBERLAIN, O. *Phys. Rev.* 1950, **77**, 305.
2. SHARRAH, P. C., PETZ, J. I. and KRUH, R. F. *J. chem. Phys.* 1960, **32**, 241.
3. VINEYARD, G. H. *J. chem. Phys.* 1954, **22**, 1665.

4. HENSHAW, D. G., HURST, D. G. and POPE, N. K.   *Phys. Rev.* 1953, **92**, 1229.
5. GINGRICH, N. S. and LE ROY HEATON.   *J. chem. Phys.* 1961, **34**, 873.
6. LEVY, H. A. *et al.*   *Ann. N.Y. Acad. Sci.* 1960, **79**, 762.
7. HURST, D. G. and HENSHAW, D. G.   *Phys. Rev.* 1955, **100**, 994.
8. HENSHAW, D. G.   *Phys. Rev.* 1957, **105**, 976.
9. HENSHAW, D. G.   *Phys. Rev.* 1958, **111**, 1470.
10. MILLIGAN, W., LEVY, H. A. and PETERSON, S. W.   *Phys. Rev.* 1951, **83**, 226.
11. WARREN, B. E.   *Phys. Rev.* 1934, **45**, 657.
12. ALCOCK, N. Z. and HURST, D. G.   *Phys. Rev.* 1949, **75**, 1609.
13. ALCOCK, N. Z. and HURST, D. G.   *Phys. Rev.* 1951, **83**, 1100.
14. HURST, D. G. and ALCOCK, N. Z.   *Can. J. Phys.* 1951, **29**, 36.
15. POPE, N. K.   *Can. J. Phys.* 1952, **30**, 597.
16. GAJEWSKI, H.   *Phys. Z.* 1932, **33**, 122.

AUTHOR INDEX

In certain cases it will be found that an author's name is not printed in the text but his work is referred to via a superscript numeral, relating to the list of references at the end of the corresponding chapter. These cases are distinguished in the list below by adding this numeral to the page number, e.g. 51[3].

SUBJECT INDEX